THE
NATURAL
WORLD

THE
NATURAL
WORLD

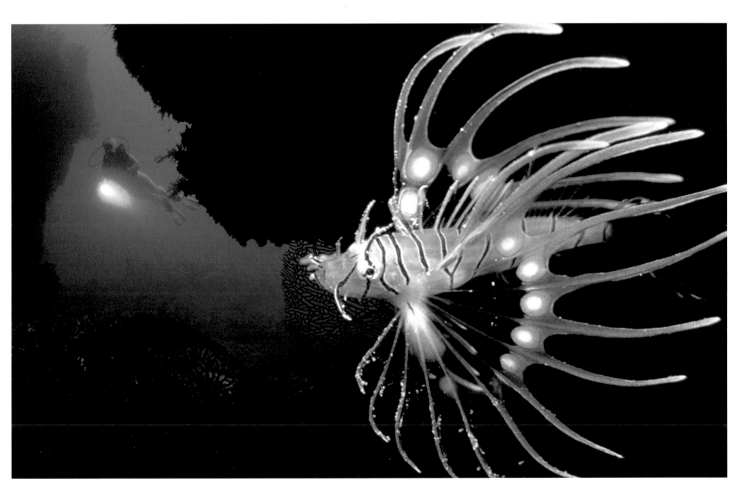

Patrick Hook

Published 2004 by Grange Books
an imprint of Grange Books PLC.
The Grange
Kings North Industrial Estate
Hoo nr. Rochester
Kent, UK
ME3 9ND

www.grangebooks.co.uk

All enquiries please email info@grangebooks.co.uk

All notations of errors or omissions (author inquiries, permissions) concerning the content of this book should be addressed to:
TAJ Books 27, Ferndown Gardens, Cobham, Surrey, UK, KT11 2BH, info@tajbooks.com.

ISBN 1-84013-726-6

Printed in China.

1 2 3 4 5 08 07 06 05 04

CONTENTS

INTRODUCTION

Red squirrels (*Tamiasciurus hudsonicus*) are solitary animals that are active in daytime throughout the year.

The natural world is a term that can be used to refer to any object or organism that is not man-made. This could include as diverse things as mountains, rivers, plants, birds, rocks or crystals. In the context of this book, however, it refers to the animal kingdom. We will examine the higher orders, from arthropods (things with jointed legs like insects, spiders and so on) upwards.

There are many living things that are not yet known to science, but all those that are—including plants—have been given scientific names. These are then organised into large groups called orders. These are then progressively split into sub-orders, families, genera and finally, species.

There are many different opinions as to how many species there are in the world. We can say that about 1.75 million have been identified and given specific names, but in real terms we have barely scratched the surface when it comes to how many others there are. It is easy to identify big things like lions

INTRODUCTION

The orangutan (*Pongo pygmaeus*) is particularly threatened in its native territories in southeast Asia due to a mixture of poaching and habitat destruction.

and elephants, but there are countless millions of microscopic organisms that live in really inaccessible places like forests and swamps. Estimates for the overall total number of different species of plants and animals range from 10 million up to a staggering 100 million.

Just because an animal has been named, it does not necessarily mean that we know anything about it, however. Even with the more recognisable ones there is still much to learn—something like 90% of the world's butterflies and moths, for instance, are only known in the adult form. That is to say that we have no idea what their caterpillars look like or what they feed on. Since something like two-thirds of all the known species in the world are insects, this means that there is still an enormous amount of

knowledge waiting to be discovered.

One of the great tragedies that is unfolding before our eyes, however, is that humans are destroying the world's natural habitats at such a rate that unknown numbers of species are being made extinct before we even know that they exist. The massive increase in the numbers of people on our small planet is putting an enormous pressure on the natural world. As a result of this there is a dire need to conserve our wild places—this has led to the creation of many conservation groups. Some of the more powerful ones have even been able to influence government policies—this is a process that we all need to support. On a positive front though, many countries have designated large areas to be natural reserves. There is a further complication, however, in that they often do not have the resources to police these areas. Illegal activities such as logging and mining are still posing a major threat to the more fragile ecosystems in many of the poorer regions of the world. Sometimes corruption is a major problem— those in power can sometimes be paid to turn a blind eye to new mines being built or even to issue official permits. When this is at the governmental level is it almost impossible to stamp out, and in this instance little can be done to save the wild habitats concerned and the animals that live in them.

It is really important to be able to know everything we can about the plants and animals around us—this way we have a chance of knowing when a species is in decline and what can be done about it. In the old days living things were classified by their form—that is what their physiological structures look like. This science is known as 'taxonomy'. In more recent times, however, the study of genetics has started to take over—this is because it is possible to trace the origins of an organism through its DNA with almost absolute certainty. This was not the case in the past, however, since deciding where an animal 'belongs' based purely on some microscopic anatomical features can be a less than exact science. Heated arguments would often rage through different academic organisations across the world as leading scientists tried to establish their views as the 'correct' interpretation of an animal's place in the classification system. These differences of opinion sometimes lasted for years, and many became very bitter. Luckily modern scientific techniques have assigned these problems to history!

In this book we will examine the five major groups of animals—these are the mammals, birds, fish, reptiles, amphibians and the invertebrates. They are accompanied by some stunning photographs which help to illustrate the incredible variety and endless beauty of the natural world.

Mammals are a very diverse group of animals which vary from the Great Apes, including Man through to hedgehogs, bats and whales. Although they are all have backbones and are warm-blooded, there are three characteristics that set them apart from all other animals - they have hair, three middle ear bones, and produce milk to feed their young. This is produced by special sweat glands called mammary glands, and is rich in protein and fats. The energy although its coloration and patterning is often used for other things as well. Camouflage is of extreme importance to prey species like deer and mice, and so they have hairs coloured to allow them to blend into the background. Skunks, on the other hand use their distinct markings to act as a visible warning for others to stay away. Colour can also convey a lot of visual information about an animal's social status. The dominant male in a group of gorillas,

The Indian or Bengal tiger (*Panthera tigris*) carrying a recent kill.

value of milk is high enough to enable the mothers of some species - especially rodents, to have very large litters and still provide enough nutrients for most of their young to survive.

Although some mammals would appear to have no hair as adults, they all possess it at some stage in their growth. The hairs themselves are composed of a protein called keratin, and are used for four main functions. For a large number of mammals the primary purpose of hair is to prevent heat loss, for instance, is known as a 'silverback', because of the colour of the hairs on its back. Hairs can also serve other specialised roles - for instance, whiskers act as sensitive sensors for lots of different species, including shrews and cats. Hairs are also used by many mammals for protection. In the porcupine, they are modified into sharp quills which provide a powerful defence mechanism. In other mammals, however, hair may only be used to prevent sunburn or abrasion by things like trees and rocks.

MAMMALS – CLASS *MAMMALIA*

Mammals are an enormously successful group of animals, and number around 5,000 species. While this figure is tiny in comparison to the countless millions of different insects, they can be found on every continent and in every sea across the world. Mammals are unlike any other class of animal in the way they vary tremendously in size and shape. They can be as small as the pygmy shrew, weighing in at only a few grams, or as they can be as large as the sea and in the air. Dolphins, seals and whales, for instance, swim in the depths of the oceans and seas of the world. Land mammals exploit almost every opportunity there is - the mole-rat, for instance, lives an entirely subterranean life. Others such as moles and myriads of small rodents will only occasionally venture above ground. Many others enjoy an arboreal existence - that is, they live in trees; these include the monkeys, lemurs, pangolins and many

The European brown bear (*Ursus arctos*).

blue whale which can be up to 150 tons in weight. The sheer size of a mammal is not necessarily an indicator as to what it feeds on, however; the tiny pygmy shrew, for instance, is a voracious hunter, whereas many whales feed on microscopic marine organisms called plankton. Some mammals like the sloth are slow moving creatures, whereas others like the rat are fast and agile.

The habitats mammals occupy range right across the spectrum - they can be found on the land, in the others. Open grasslands are the preferred habitat of things like zebra and bison, whereas thick forests are the abode of choice for animals like tigers and tapirs. The air is used by some mammals like the flying squirrel as a method of moving across forest glades or evading predators. In many places the air is often thick with flying insects, and this valuable food resource is exploited by bats which spend large amounts of time flying freely through the air catching everything from mosquitoes to moths.

MAMMALS – CLASS *MAMMALIA*

The Polar bear (*Ursus maritimus*).

Mammals are diverse in their feeding habits, although they all fall into three basic categories. There are those which are exclusively herbivores - that is, they eat only plant matter; these include gorillas, deer, giraffe and horses. Many other mammals are omnivores, consuming both plants and animals - these tend to be opportunists, and will eat almost anything they can find which is edible; examples include humans, and rodents. On the other hand, a large number of mammals are exclusively carnivorous, that is, they are meat eaters. These include dolphins, lions, tigers, the micro bats, and hedgehogs.

Although mammals are very numerous, many of them are under intense survival pressure and lots are close to extinction. The Ganges river dolphin, for example, is particularly close to disappearing for all time. In the last hundred years or so we have lost many remarkable mammalian species, ranging from the South African Quagga, a type of zebra that became extinct in the late 19th century to the last Australian Thylacine or Tasmanian Tiger which died in 1936. In the 20th century we also lost at least four species of bats, as well as the Caribbean monk seal, which was last seen in 1952.

Most of the survival pressures on land mammals

When a lion pride goes off hunting the young have to be guarded by a couple of adults to protect them against attacks by other lions or smaller predators such as hyenas.

come from loss of habitat, due to human activities such as logging, mining or deforestation for agricultural purposes. In the case of marine mammals, however, the biggest problem is typically pollution. An oil tanker spill can wipe out the ecology of an entire river system, and if a species (such as the Ganges river dolphin) only inhabits a single waterway it is especially vulnerable. Many whale species came close to extinction as a result of commercial hunting, and it was only when this was banned internationally that matters improved. Sadly, there are several countries that want to starting

whaling on a large scale again, although world-wide condemnation may be enough to prevent this from happening. If you feel passionately about this, then you can make your voice heard by joining one or more of the many conservation societies dedicated to this purpose.

The largest bottle-nosed dolphins occur off Great Britain, where an adult can weigh as much as 1,430lb (650kg); in other parts of the world, however, most are much smaller.

Whales & Dolphins

Whales and dolphins are in the order Cetacea, and are amongst the most popular animals on the planet. Not only are they supremely majestic, but they are highly intelligent. They were, however, seen by mankind as a simple commodity until fairly recently. For early humans they represented an enormous bounty–depending on the animal's size, a single kill could feed anything from a few families to a whole tribe. The annual toll back then was negligible; however, when commercial whaling got established some three hundred years ago, the situation changed dramatically. Many species were hunted so remorselessly that they teetered on the edge of extinction. Thankfully, international pressure managed to stop the trade, and apart from a few rogue nations who are trying to start whaling again, these days it is seen as an unacceptable practice. In its place, whale watching has grown up as a tourist industry, and many fishermen who would have previously hunted and killed whales now have a vested interest in keeping them alive.

Although whales and dolphins are usually seen as gentle creatures, there are many species which are ferocious hunters. The most famous is undoubtedly the killer whale–these are large black and white marine mammals which often hunt in packs on anything from shoals of herring to newly born whale calves.

The bottle-nosed dolphin (*Tursiops truncatus*) is the species most commonly seen along the shores of Europe and the United States.

DOLPHIN

The bottle-nosed dolphin is named after its short and stubby beak which is well equipped with teeth to catch the fish and squid on which it feeds.

Dolphin – Red Sea

There are several subspecies of bottle-nose dolphins in the world—this one is the Red Sea variant (*Tursiops truncatus aduncus*).

COMMON DOLPHIN

The common dolphin (Delphinus delphis) is found in all the tropical and sub-tropical seas of the world. This image shows just how well suited they are to high speeds in water.

An overhead view of a blue whale in the open sea
near San Diego shows the blue-gray skin which
gives this massive animal its name.

MAMMALS – CLASS *MAMMALIA*

GRAY WHALE

The Californian gray whale (*Eschrichtius robustus*) is a popular draw for tourists when it comes close inshore to breed.

GRAY WHALE CALF

This young gray whale calf which was born near Monterey in California will need its mother's protection as it will be vulnerable to attack by killer whales.

For reasons not properly understood, the humpback whale often makes spectacular leaps from the water—this process is known as 'breaching.'

HUMPBACK WHALE

The humpback whale feeds on small shrimp-like crustaceans and small fish. Each individual eats up to 1.5 tons (1,524kg) of food a day.

BLUE WHALE
When the blue whale exhales a tall plume of water spray is released. This action is known as a 'blow.'

Risso's dolphin (*Grampus griseus*) is also known as the Grampus dolphin. It is an offshore species that lives in tropical and temperate seas

Blue Whale

The blue whale (*Balaenoptera musculus*) grows to a maximum length of c90ft (27m) and a weight of 150 tons (152,400kg)—making it the largest living animal in the world. Here a mother can be seen next to her calf.

SPOTTED DOLPHINS

There are two different species of spotted dolphins; one ranges worldwide, and is called *Stenella attenuata*; the other, seen here, is the Atlantic spotted dolphin (*Stenella frontalis*).

The sperm whale (*Physeter macrocephalus*) has been hunted commercially for many years. Here two victims of this appalling trade are being towed into an Icelandic whaling station.

This white-sided dolphin (*Lagenorhynchus obliquidens*) swimming near San Diego has collected some seaweed in a display of the latest cetacean fashionwear.

Mammals – Class *Mammalia*

Primates

Apes and monkeys belong to the order of primates. They are fascinating creatures with a wide range of size and shape. From the smaller species, such as the cotton top tamarin and the slow loris, to the enormous bulk of the gorilla, they are all highly intelligent, and usually very social animals. For many years there was a large trade in apes and monkeys—these were either destined for the pet trade or, even worse, for the medical experimentation industry. The vast majority of these were taken from the wild—often the easiest way was simply to kill breeding monkeys and collect their helpless youngsters. Although this practice has been made illegal in most countries, it still continues in many places. Unfortunately, the rarest species inevitably

commanded the highest prices, and so this put great pressure on already threatened animals. The golden lion tamarin, for instance, was already suffering from habitat loss, and collecting pushed it close to disappearing from the wild altogether.

Fortunately, these and other endangered primates are being successfully bred in captivity, and where their natural habitats can either be preserved or restored, they are being released into the wild. In these instances there is hope that the population of these rare species can once again reach self-sustaining levels.

The western lowland gorilla (*Gorilla gorilla*) is an endangered species which is being bred in captivity with the hope that there will be enough young produced to release into the wild.

SLOW LORIS

The slow loris (*Nycticebus coucang*) is a rare nocturnal primate which lives in rainforests from Vietnam to Borneo.

Considering that the western lowland gorilla only eats vegetation, the silverback male is an incredibly powerfully built animal.

CHIMPANZEE

The chimpanzee (*Pan troglodytes*) is under threat from poachers who will often kill adults for meat and then sell any youngsters they can catch to the pet trade.

LONGTAILED MACAQUE

The long-tailed macaque or crab-eating monkey (*Macaca fascicularis*) is found in southeast Asia from Burma to the Philippines.

Hamadryas Baboon

This is a male Hamadryas baboon (*Papio hamadryas*) from Ethopia. These baboons live in large groups with complicated social structures.

PILEATED GIBBON

The pileated gibbon (*Hylobates pileatus*) can be found in Borneo where it likes to swing through the rainforest canopy at great speed.

Pigtailed Macaque

The pigtailed macaque (*Macaca nemestrina*), named after its short thin tail, is getting increasingly rare in the wild. It eats mostly fruits and other vegetation.

SQUIRREL MONKEY

The squirrel monkey (*Saimiri sciureus*) is an opportunist that will eat fruit, flowers, and leaves as well as any small animals it can catch.

The green monkey (*Cercopithecus aethiops*) is also known as the vervet or tantalus monkey. It is highly adaptable and can live in a variety of habitats including living alongside humans.

Mammals - Class *Mammalia*

Spider Monkey

The spider monkey (*Ateles geoffroyi*) is an incredibly agile species which lives in the rainforests of South America—this example was photographed in Belize.

GOLDEN LION TAMARIN

The golden lion tamarin (*Leontopithecus rosalia*) is an extremely endangered primate—mostly this is because of habitat loss, but also due to being hunted for the pet trade

COQUEREL'S DWARF LEMUR

Coquerel's dwarf lemur (*Microcebus coquereli*) is a nocturnal primate which spends the first part of the night feeding on small vertebrates and vegetable matter—then it socializes until dawn.

CROWNED LEMUR

The crowned lemur (*Eulemur coronatus*) is normally active by day, but will also forage for leaves and fruit at night.

Ringtailed lemurs (*Lemur catta*) are endemic to Madagascar—they enjoy sitting in the sun on their haunches, and curl into a ball to sleep.

Verreaux's Sifaka

Verreaux's sifaka (*Propithelus verreauxi*) is a nocturnal tree-dwelling Madagascan primate with characteristic white fur and a long tail.

HANUMAN LANGUR

The Hanuman langur (*Presbytis entellus*) is an Indian monkey with strong social patterns. Here a mother cares for her baby

Marsupials

Marsupials (order Marsupialia) are, for the most part, restricted to Australasia. Opossums are the main exception, for these strange-looking creatures are also distributed across the Americas. The others— kangaroos, koalas, wombats, wallabies and so on— evolved in isolation from the fauna and flora of the rest of the world. As a result, the marsupials are quite unlike animals found elsewhere. Sadly, mankind's activities have resulted in the loss of many unique animals—this started when the first humans settled on the Australian mainland, many thousands of years ago. These people, who developed into the aborigines we know today, brought dogs with them and used grassland fires to hunt on a large scale. Many of the indigenous animals, which had never seen humans before, were totally unequipped to cope and were soon hunted to extinction. The arrival of vast numbers of people over the last hundred years or so has been a catastrophe for Australian wildlife. Not only has there been massive habitat loss for agricultural purposes, but the importation of dogs, cats, foxes and many other alien animals has wiped out many marsupial species.

When early European explorers first started investigating the fauna and flora of Australia, they reported seeing many wonderful animals. The scientists at home, however, often refused to believe that animals as bizarre as the descriptions could possibly exist. Probably the ultimate example of this was the duck-billed platypus, which was declared to be a hoax when the first specimens arrived in Europe.

Adult koalas are mostly solitary and have permanent territories, although that of the male will overlap those of several nearby females.

MARSUPIALS – ORDER *MARSUPIALIA*

VIRGINIA OPOSSUM

The common or Virginia opossum (*Didelphis virginana*) is a tree-dwelling marsupial with a prehensile tail. It has a long nose and is equipped with lots of sharp teeth.

The koala (*Phascolarctos cinereus*) is an Australian species which feeds almost exclusively on eucalyptus. Since its diet has little nutritional value it moves very slowly to conserve energy.

MAMMALS – CLASS *MAMMALIA*

SWAMP WALLABY

The swamp wallaby (*Wallabia bicolor*) is an Australian marsupial that is much smaller than the kangaroo. It lives in damp grassland areas.

TASMANIAN DEVIL

The Tasmanian devil (*Sarcophlus harrisii*) is the largest marsupial carnivore. It is an aggressive nocturnal animal which is equipped with powerful jaws.

Kowari

The kowari (*Dasycercus byrnei*) is a small Australian marsupial which lives in burrows. Its diet consists of insects, spiders and other small animals such as birds, rodents, and lizards.

Marsupials – Order *Marsupialia*

Common Wombat

The common wombat (*Vombatus ursinus*) is a powerfully built marsupial which forages for food on the ground of the Australian forests and woods where it lives.

The red kangaroo (*Megaleta rufa*) is native to the Australian continent where it breeds so successfully that it has become an agricultural pest.

CATS

There are many different species of cats in the wild, all of which belong to the order Carnivora, and the family Felidae. They range in size from the small hunting cats of Africa to the enormous Bengal tigers of Asia. As species, all of them face pressures of one kind or another. Hunting with guns and traps was responsible for the deaths of large numbers of the more visible cats—especially lions and tigers; however, the biggest single threat to them all these days is habitat loss. As the size of the global human population increases, more and more wild places are being destroyed to build houses or to create new farmland. Fortunately, there are many organisations around the world which are now trying to conserve the natural landscape, and others are attempting to improve the situation by implementing captive breeding programmes. In the past zoos were simply places where people went to see what certain animals looked like. When animals died, they just got some more. This is no longer the case, and many are doing a fantastic job in helping conserve threatened species.

This is well illustrated by the example of some of the smaller feline species. Many are interbreeding with domestic cats, which is a serious problem that is very hard to prevent—as a result, several species are now more threatened than ever. The population of these animals held in the zoos of the world now represents an irreplaceable gene pool—they may yet prove to be the salvation of many species which could otherwise go extinct.

The Bengal or Indian tiger (*Panthera tigris*) is such an efficient hunter that it needs a massive territory—consequently the only time tigers meet intentionally is for mating.

SIBERIAN TIGER

The Siberian tiger (*Panthera tigris altaica*) is an extremely endangered species which is another subject of successful captive breeding programmes.

ASIAN LION

Most people think of the lion as being an African species—there is, however, another which comes from Asia; shown here is a female Asian lion (*Panthera leo persica*).

LION

The lion (*Panthera leo*) is the dominant carnivore of much of the African continent. Although the male is the more powerful of the sexes, it is the female that does most of the hunting.

When a leopard makes a kill, it has to get the carcass off the ground as soon as possible to avoid having it snatched by hyenas.

LEOPARD

The leopard (*Panthera pardus*) is a powerful hunter, although since it is usually solitary it cannot compete with lions and has to give way when it encounters them.

CLOUDED LEOPARD

The clouded leopard (*Neofelis nebulosa*), the smallest of the big cats, occurs in south Asia. It regularly uses its excellent climbing skills in its search for prey.

OCELOT

The ocelot (*Felis pardalis*) is a small South American cat which feeds on a variety of small mammals and birds, although it will take reptiles, amphibians, and fish if it gets the chance.

CATS - ORDER *CARNIVORA*

BOBCAT

The bobcat (*Felis rufus*) grows to a maximum of 2ft (0.6m) tall and a weight of about 20lb (9kg). They are solitary nocturnal hunters which will prey on anything they can manage to kill.

The cheetah (*Acinonyx jubatus*) is the fastest
land animal on Earth—short bursts at speeds
of up to 70mph have been recorded for this
beautiful cat.

FEMALE BOBCAT

The female bobcat is very protective when she has young—here some five week old cubs are being nursed by their attentive mother.

JUNGLE CAT

The jungle cat (*Felis chaus*) is a rarely seen species which hunts for small prey animals in the forests and grasslands of India.

The wildcat (*Felis silvestris*) is extremely endangered in the wild due to the threat from cross-breeding with domestic cats.

BLACK PANTHER

The black jaguar or black panther (*Panthera onca*) is usually found in dense forests where it preys on animals of all sizes from small rodents to caiman crocodiles.

PUMA

The puma is a fierce predator which will take deer, bighorn sheep, mountain goats, hares, and even mice. This individual has just pounced on a deer.

Puma

The puma (*Felis concolor*) is also known as the cougar or mountain lion. It is distributed throughout North and South America.

LYNX

This seven-week old lynx (*Lynx canadensis*) cub will grow up to be a ferocious hunter of all sorts of small animals, including birds, rabbits and rodents.

Mammals - Class Mammalia

Bears

There is something about bears that humans take to very easily. Whether it is because we play with teddy bears from our earliest years or not is hard to say, but whatever the reason, they are very popular creatures. They feature in everything from children's stories and fairy tales to Greek legends and modern movies. Most of us will never see a bear in the wild, and this is probably a good thing as humans and wild bears do not mix well. Bears, which belong to the order Carnivora, family Ursidae, are immensely powerful animals which for the large part are more than capable of killing or injuring people. They are often very territorial, and are able to run much faster then we can. They are great opportunists, and most will eat anything they come across—this can include things they forage for, such as nuts, berries, roots and eggs, as well as things they hunt, from fish to large animals. In places like Alaska, polar bears often come into conflict with humans when they enter villages looking for food. Likewise, grizzly bears have been known to kill and eat unwary backpackers or fishermen. Most bears, however, just want to be left alone, and will run away if they detect the merest hint of humans!

The European brown bear (*Ursus arctos*) is a large predatory carnivore which lives in dense woodland. It is listed as an endangered species.

BLACK BEAR

The black bear (*Ursus americanus*) is the best known and most widespread of the North American bears. It usually grows to 135–350lb (60–160kg) in weight.

The grizzly bear (*Ursus arctos*) will eat fruit and berries, however, it will also eat anything it can kill—here a large individual is seen taking advantage of the salmon's annual spawning run.

MAMMALS - CLASS *MAMMALIA*

HYENAS & THE WEASEL FAMILY

This group of animals covers a wide range of species. They are all member of the order Carnivora—the carnivores—but whereas the hyenas belong to the Hyaenidae family, all the others—the badgers, skunk, otters, stoat, mink and weasel—all belong to the Mustelidae family. While all these animals are capable of being voracious hunters, some, such as the badger, will also on occasion eat vegetable matter in the form of roots and bulbs. Hyenas are pack hunters, and groups of them can present a formidable presence on the plains of Africa. Even a pride of lions will give way and allow a kill to be taken from them if enough hyenas turn up. Badgers are also social animals, but like the other members of the mustelidae family, for the most part they tend to hunt singly. This is because the food they eat is usually too scattered to feed more than one animal at a time. Mink are also solitary animals except when breeding—they have been farmed for many years, from where unfortunately, many have either been deliberately released or they have escaped. These animals have wreaked havoc with the natural fauna, as they have few natural predators in most of the regions where they have recently become established.

The spotted hyena (*Crocuta crocuta*) is one of the dominant animals of the African savannah—even lions have to give up their kills when a pack of hyenas appears.

AMERICAN BADGER

The American badger (*Taxidea taxus*) has powerful legs which allow it to dig the extensive burrows in which it lives and raises its young.

Spotted hyenas are not just scavengers on other animals kills—they also hunt very effectively using their powerful jaws to overcome their prey.

SKUNK

The striped skunk (*Mephitis mephitis*) is an American animal which uses a powerful and highly unpleasant odour as a very effective defence mechanism.

Stoat

The stoat (*Mustela erminea*), which is also known as the ermine, is a highly efficient predator of birds, rodents, rabbits, and all manner of other small animals.

The otter (*Lutra lutra*) is one of the first species to suffer when pollution spills occur. A healthy otter population therefore indicates a healthy river.

MINK

The mink (*Mustela vison*) has been bred for fur in many places across the world. Unfortunately, many have escaped causing havoc with the local wildlife.

WEASEL

The weasel (*Mustela nivalis*) is a small predator which hunts rodents, birds, and almost any other animals it can manage to overpower and kill.

WOLVES, DOGS, CIVETS & FOXES

The animals covered in this section are all in the order Carnivora. The jackals, dogs, dingoes, coyotes, wolves and foxes all fall into the Canidae family, whereas the racoon, red panda and coatimundi are members of the Procyonidae family. The giant panda, which belongs to the Ailuropodidae family is a bit of an oddity in many ways. Being a member of the carnivora, it would be logical to expect it to be a carnivore; however, it only eats bamboo leaves. It has become the symbol of the World Wildlife Fund, and as such it has come to represent the plight of so many of the endangered animals on our planet. It is in itself extremely endangered, although modern advances in human fertilisation treatments have recently been successfully used to increase vastly the number of young pandas born in captive breeding establishments. Foxes, racoons and coatimundis are all opportunists, and will take advantage of more or less any feeding opportunities that present themselves. They will all readily scavenge from human refuse given the chance, and this adaptability has lead to them becoming established in many urban and suburban areas. Wolves are generally far less tolerant of people, although there have been occasions when individual animals have taken up residence alongside human settlements.

The jackal (*Canis aureus*) is a social animal which hunts in packs—these individuals are fighting over prey in their native Indian jungle.

ASIAN WILD DOG

The Asian wild dog (*Cuon alpinus*) is an endangered species which lives in packs in tropical rainforests. They are efficient killers which makes them unpopular with local humans.

It is thought that the dingo (*Canis familiaris*) was introduced to Australia by early human settlers. The last remaining wild population is to be found on Fraser Island.

EUROPEAN WOLF

The European wolf (*Canis lupus*) has been reintroduced into the wild in several countries where it is making a slow comeback.

GRAY WOLF

The timber or gray wolf (*Canis Lupus*) is an American species which is smaller and less aggressive than its European counterpart.

Coyote

The coyote (*Canius latrans*) is similar to but smaller than the wolf; it is often hunted and trapped illegally—this poor individual has been caught in a gin trap in New Mexico.

Fox

The fox (*Vulpes vulpes*) has made a successful transition from being a rural hunter to an urban scavenger. This individual is raiding a dustbin and feeding on household rubbish.

The fennec fox (*Vulpes zerda*) is a very small desert fox that has large ears which assist in finding its prey. It has furred soles which help it walk on soft sand.

Bat-eared Fox

The bat-eared fox (*Otocyon megalotis*) is found in arid grasslands and savannahs. Its range extends from Sudan down to South Africa.

AFRICAN HUNTING DOG

The African hunting dog (*Lycaon pictus*) was once a common species—although poaching has reduced their numbers, diseases caught from domestic dogs have almost wiped them out.

MAMMALS – CLASS *MAMMALIA*

RACOON

The racoon (*Procyonlotor spp*) is the ultimate opportunist, happily living right alongside humans throughout the United States.

COATIMUNDI

The coatimundi (*Nasua nasua*) has a long snout which it uses to search for spiders and other small creatures under stones and amongst leaf litter.

RED PANDA

The red panda (*Ailurus fulgens*) is much smaller than its relation the giant panda. It is solitary and spends much of its time living in trees.

GIANT PANDA

The giant panda (*Ailuropoda melanoleuca*) is one of the best known endangered animals. It is especially vulnerable because it feeds exclusively in endangered bamboo forests.

MAMMALS - CLASS *MAMMALIA*

SEALS

The seals belong to three distinct families—the Otariidae family includes the eared seals, such as the fur seal and the sea lions. The walrus belongs to the Odobenidae family, and the true or earless seals belong to the Phocidae family. The true seals include the leopard, grey, Weddell, and elephant seals. The largest by a long way is the male elephant seal, which can reach 15ft (4.5m) long and weigh as much as 8,800lb (4,000kg). The females are much smaller and only reach about a fifth of this weight. Both sexes feed on fish and cephalopods, as do the Weddell seals. The Leopard seal, which reaches around 1,000lb (450kg), however, is a large predator with a preference for the much smaller crabeater seals and Adelie penguins. If there is nothing else to feed on though, they will take krill instead. The walrus is different to most seals in that it mainly feeds on crustaceans, molluscs, starfish and sea urchins. On the whole, seals are not particularly endangered, as their habitats are reasonably stable, and apart from occasional incidents, rarely come into conflict with mankind. There have, however, been sporadic outbreaks of disease in certain species which have reduced their populations alarmingly.

The leopard seal (*Hydrurga leptonyx*) is an Antarctic species that is a powerful predator of penguins and other seals.

WEDDELL SEAL

The Antarctic or Weddell seal (*Leptonychotes weddelli*) is a big animal—it can grow to nearly eight feet long and weigh up to c900lb (400kg).

The male southern elephant seal (*Mirounga leonina*) is an enormous animal—these two have hauled themselves onto a beach in South Georgia and are fighting over territory.

WALRUS

The walrus (*Odobenus rosmarus*) is a large marine mammal that is equipped with a large set of tusks—it lives in the Arctic where it used to be hunted for its ivory.

CALIFORNIAN SEA LION

The Californian sea lion (*Zalophus californianus*) is found along the coast from California to Mexico, as well as in the Galapagos Islands and in the southern Sea of Japan.

The gray seal (*Halichoerus grypus*) can be found on the coasts of both sides of the Atlantic Ocean. They tend to breed on small islands away from predators.

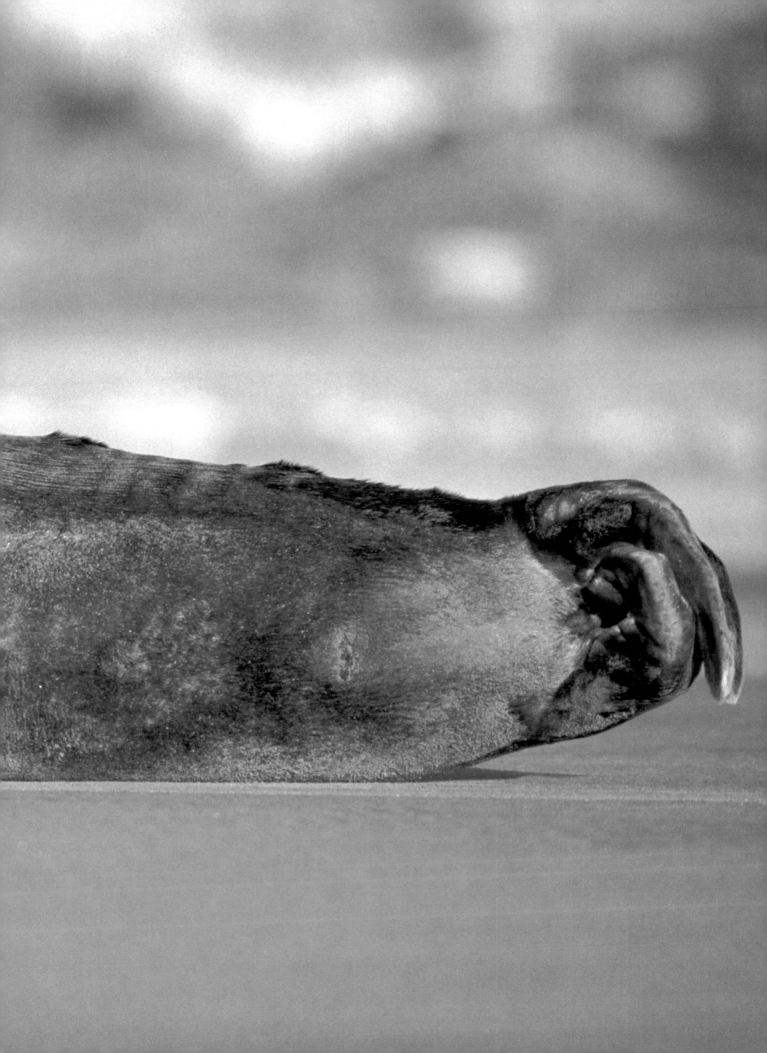

ELEPHANTS

Until recently it was thought that there were only two species of elephant alive today—these were the African elephant and the Asian elephant (sometimes called the Indian elephant). Genetic testing, however, has proved that the African Forest elephant, which was previously thought to be a subspecies, is in fact an entirely distinct species in its own right. It is smaller than its savannah dwelling counterpart, with males only rarely reaching any more than 8ft (2.5m) in height. In comparison, a large bull savannah elephant can reach nearly 13ft (4 m) in height and weigh up to 14,330lb (6,500kg). It is estimated that around a third of all the African elephants are actually forest elephants. The Asian elephant is easy to identify because it has quite small ears—the African species both have very large ears indeed. All three of these amazing creatures belong to the order Proboscidea, in the family Elephantidae. The elephant has been an integral part of human culture across the Asian continent since history was first recorded. Their incredible strength and great intelligence has been exploited by mankind for everything from moving timber to acting as mobile war platforms.

The bull African elephant (*Loxodonta africana*) does not tolerate any animals that could pose a threat to the herd, such as the baboon being chased away here.

AFRICAN ELEPHANT

Before an bull African elephant attacks it will usually adopt an aggressive threat posture—this is signaled by a combination of a hunched stance and splayed ears.

ASIAN ELEPHANT
The Asian elephant (*Elephas maximus*) has smaller ears and is not as big overall as its African cousin. It occurs in many of the forested regions of the Asian continent.

ASIAN ELEPHANT

Asian elephants are often used to help humans carry out tasks that require sheer strength, such as pulling up trees and carrying timber.

MAMMALS - CLASS *MAMMALIA*

HERBIVORES

The animals covered in this section are all herbivores that fall into one of three orders. The smallest of these is the order Sirenia, which includes the West Indian manatee—this is a large, but gentle, marine mammal which is sometimes referred to as the sea-cow. The Perissodactyla is a much larger order, and includes the horses, ponies, zebra, tapirs and rhinoceros. Some of these, like the horse, have been enormously important to mankind for thousands of years. Others, like the tapir, have had little significance in human history other than as occasional food to native American indians. The third order, the Artiodactyla, is also a large grouping, and includes the oryx, gazelle, bison, wildebeest, giraffe, antelope, hippopotamus, camel, llama, guanaco, deer, moose, pig, warthog and peccary. Some of the herbivores, such as many of the species of deer, are very common, but others such as the rhinoceros are extremely endangered. The animals listed here come from every continent except Antarctica. The llama, guanaco and tapir all come from South America, for instance, whereas the zebra and giraffe hail from Africa. The pronghorn antelope is exclusively North American, but there are other species of deer which range right around the globe, from Europe, across Asia and into the Americas.

Captive breeding is one solution to increasing the numbers of endangered species such as this Indian rhino which was bred at Marwell Zoo in the United Kingdom.

BLACK RHINO

The black rhinoceros (*Diceros bicornis*) has suffered the most drastic population decline of all rhino species. Recent conservation efforts have helped improve matters.

The blue wildebeest or brindled gnu (*Connochaetes taurinus*) gathers in large groups to graze on the grassland savannahs of Eastern Africa.

White Arabian ponies in Virginia.

Burchell's zebra (*Equus burchelli burchelli*) is one of four subspecies of zebra found on the grasslands of East Africa. Here a group can be seen drinking at a water hole.

Oryx

The most successful populations of the oryx (*Oryx beisa*) are in remote places—this magnificent individual blends well against the red sands of the Namib Desert.

PRONGHORN ANTELOPE

The pronghorn antelope (*Antilocapra americana*) is unique in that it is the only animal in the world with branched horns (as opposed to antlers).

The Masai giraffe (*Giraffa camelopardalis tippelskirchi*) seen here feeding on Acacia leaves is one of nine subspecies of giraffe.

H

The
cam

The hippopotamus (*Hippopotamus amphibus*) used to be found throughout tropical Africa, but human activity has now meant that it is mostly restricted to game parks and reserves.

The dromedary camel (*Camelus dromedarius*) is a herbivorous desert quadruped—these days most are domesticated and are fed by people.

The spotted deer is a native of India—the individual seen here is a youngster which is hiding from potential predators by using its camouflage to blend in with fallen leaves.

RED DEER

Red deer (*Cervus elatus*) live in the mountains and moorlands of the Palearctic region where life can be very harsh in the winter. This stag was photographed on a hillside in Scotland.

REINDEER

The reindeer (*Rangifer tarandus*) comes from the Arctic where it feeds on grasses, mosses, and lichens in the harsh tundra habitats.

The moose (*Alces alces*) is a large herbivore that is common in
the wilder areas of North America. This mother with her calf
was photographed in the Rocky Mountain National Park.

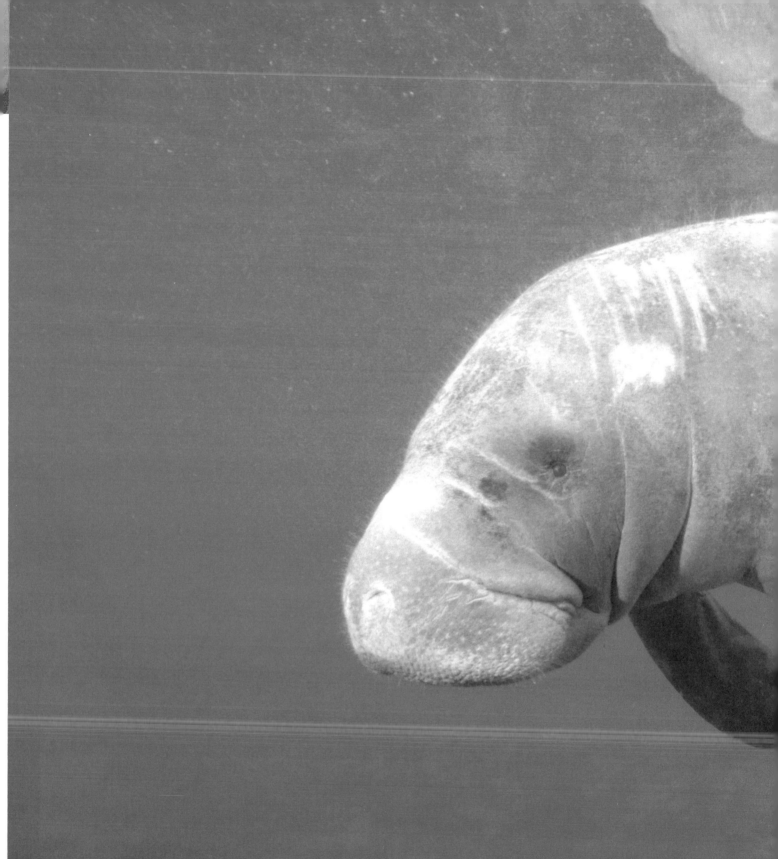

The West Indian manatee (*Trechechus manatus*) is also known as the sea cow. It is a gentle herbivore which is found in shallow waters where it feeds on sea grass.

The population of bison (*Bison bison*) in the
United States once numbered in the hundreds
of thousands, but hunting on an unjustifiable
scale brought it close to extinction.

INSECTIVORES

The animals which have been included in this section come from six distinct families—five from the order Insectivora, and one from the order Monotremata. These are the Tenrecidae family (the common tenrec), the Tupaiidae (the common tree shrew), the Soricidae (the pigmy shrew), the Talpidae (the mole), the Erinaceidae (the hedgehog), and the Tachyglossidae (the echidna). It is interesting to note that although they look very similar, the hedgehog and the echidna are completely unrelated. The echidna is a monotreme, and as such is much closer to a platypus than anything other living animal, while the hedgehog is allied to all the others discussed here except the tree shrew. The reason these two prickly creatures look much alike is that they both fill similar ecological niches—both are specially adapted to hunt for small ground-dwelling animals. The most efficient form of defence for both of them was to grow spines, and so even though they evolved on separate continents, they ended up with similar solutions to the same problem. The insectivores get their name from the fact that most of the are exclusively insect eaters; some like the mole spend most of their lives underground, whereas others, like the tree shrew, are arboreal.

The hedgehog (*Erinaceus europaeus*) is a European insectivore which eats slugs, snails, insects, worms and fallen fruit. However, they will also attack mice, lizards, frogs and snakes

ECHIDNA

The echidna (*Tachyglossus aculeatus*) which is also known as the spiny anteater, is a solitary animal that hunts for ants nests where it finds its prey by smell.

The common tenrec (*Tenrec ecaudatus*) is an insectivore that only occurs in Madagascar. It has a long snout on which there are sensitive whiskers which help it to find food.

MAMMALS – CLASS *MAMMALIA*

COMMON TREE SHREW

The common tree shrew (*Tupaia glis*) is a small squirrel-like insectivore which inhabits the tropical forests of southeast Asia.

PYGMY SHREW

The pymgy shrew (*Sorex minutus*) is the smallest mammal found in the British Isles. It has a very short digestive tract and so has to feed every few minutes.

The common mole (*Talpa europaea*) has a powerful body, which is about 7in (18cm) long, and soft, dark fur. It is almost blind and lives underground in long tunnels.

The wrinkle-lipped Bat (*Chaerephon plicata*) is
a species which roosts in huge numbers—when
they emerge at dusk to feed, their swarms can
number many thousands.

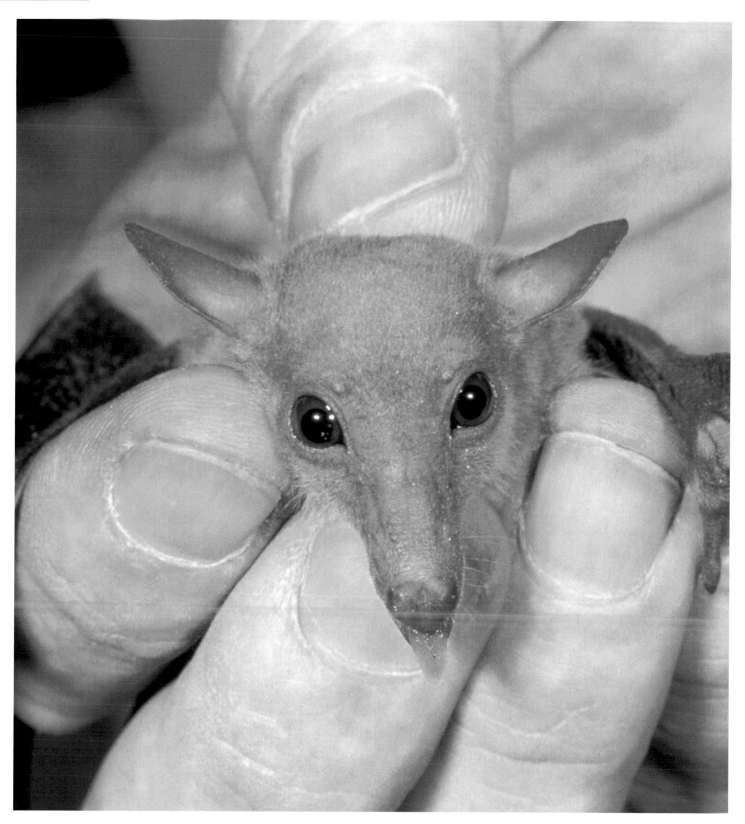

Long-Tongued Nectar Bat

The greater long-tongued nectar bat (*Macroglossus sobrinus*) is an Indonesian species which feeds on the nectar from large flowers.

LONG-EARED BAT

The common long-eared bat (Plecotus auritus) is very common in the temperate parts of the Palearctic Region. This one is being cared for in a wildlife hospital after being injured.

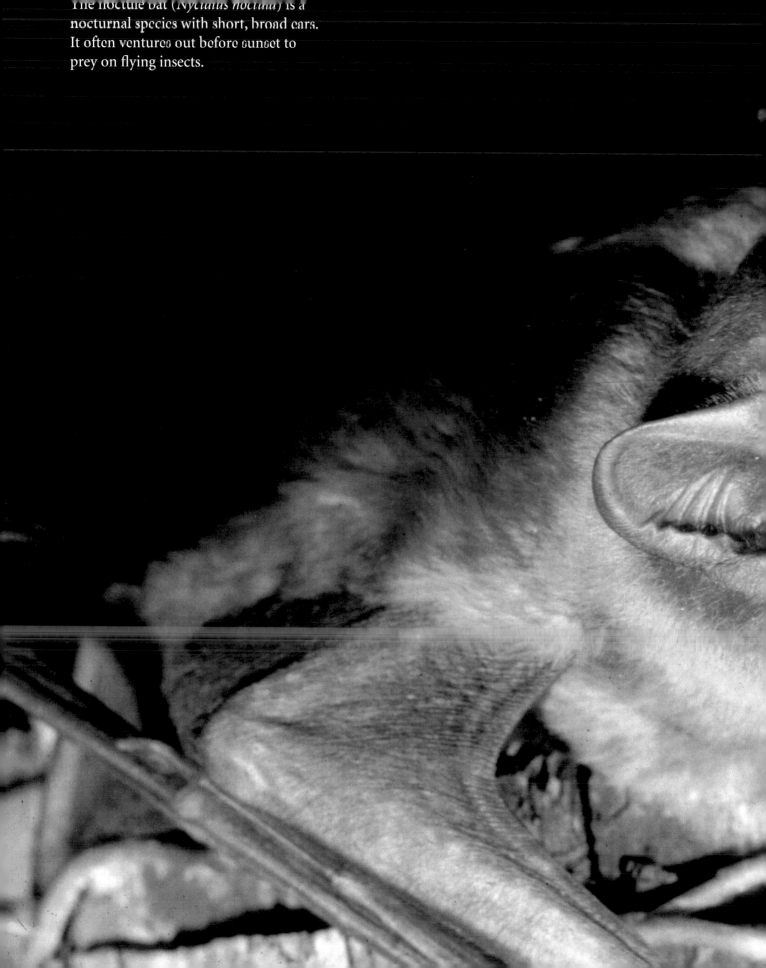

The noctule bat (*Nyctalus noctula*) is a nocturnal species with short, broad ears. It often ventures out before sunset to prey on flying insects.

The giant ground pangolin (*Manis gigantea*) has a long, tapering body that is almost completely covered with virtually impenetrable overlapping scales.

RABBITS & RODENTS

While rabbits and rodents can be considered to be very similar kinds of animals, they are actually classified in separate orders. The rabbits and hares are in the family Leporidae, which is one of only two families in the order Lagomorpha; there are 63 species of lagomorphs world-wide. The rodents, however, are grouped into 30 different families which together form the order Rodentia.

The examples included in this section come from the Sciuridae, Castoridae, Muridae, Hystricidae and Hydrochaeridae families. In all there are about 1,600 different species of rodents, which makes this the largest grouping in the mammalian kingdom. Rabbits and the larger rodents do have many things in common, however. They are all gnawing mammals with a single large pair of incisor teeth which are specialised for eating vegetation. Indeed, they have to keep gnawing at things to wear their teeth down as they continue to grow throughout their lives. To escape from predators, rabbits and hares have legs which are specialised for high-speed escape. Mice and prairie dogs usually disappear below ground at the first sight of trouble, whereas beavers build a fortified nest where they rear their young. Porcupines, however, don't bother to try and escape—instead they defend themselves very effectively with a mass of extremely sharp quills.

The rabbit (*Onyctolagus cuniculus*) has such a high breeding rate that when uncontrolled by predators it quickly becomes a serious agricultural pest.

BROWN HARE

The brown hare (*Lepus europaeus*) is much larger than its close relative, the rabbit. For most of the year hares are solitary, and only assemble in numbers at the start of the mating season.

HOARY MARMOT
The hoary marmot (*Marmota caligata*) is distributed along the mountain ranges of western North America. This individual was photographed in the Yosemite National Park.

GROUNDHOG

The groundhog or woodchuck (*Marmota monax*) is one of the few animals which has prospered as a result of human activity—it prefers open farmland to thick forests.

Porcupine

The common short-tailed porcupine (*Hystrix brachyura*) from southeast Asia is smaller than its African relative and also has fewer quills.

RABBITS & RODENTS – ORDER *RODENTIA*, *LAGOMORPHA*

HARVEST MOUSE

The once-common harvest mouse (*Micromys minutus*) is an agile climber and makes its spherical nest high up in tall grasses.

The African brush-tailed porcupine (*Atherurus africanus*) is nocturnal and has long black and white quills—these are extremely sharp and provide a very effective defense.

SPINY MOUSE

The spiny mouse (*Aconys cahirinus*) is named after the stiff hairs on its back and tail. It is a nocturnal forager which uses its excellent hearing to avoid predators.

CAPYBARA

The capybara (*Hydrochoereus hydrochaeris*) is the largest living rodent—it is semi-aquatic, and lives in groups alongside rivers and lakes in Central and South America.

FISH – CLASS *CHONDRICHTHYES, ACTINOPTERYGII*

Fish form a fascinating and complex part of the animal kingdom—few authors agree on how their classification should be arranged. There are four main groupings, these are the Agnathans or jawless fish (which are divided into the Myxini and Cephalospidomorpha), the extinct Placodermi or scaly-skinned fish, the Chondrichthyes or cartilaginous fish, and the Osteichthyes or bony fish (which are split into the Sarcopterygii and Actinopterygii).

The Agnathans differ from all other vertebrates in that they do not possess a jaw—they survive without this normally vital structure by living as parasites and scavengers. There are only two groups of jawless fish alive today—these are the hagfish and the lampreys, of which there are 45 extant species in total; there used to be a third called the Ostracoderms, but they are only known from fossil remains. These strange fish have many other unusual characteristics; for instance, they only have vestigial vision—this is provided by light sensitive structures known as pineal eyes. Their digestive system also lacks a stomach, and so they have very specialised feeding habits. Hagfish, for instance, hide themselves in mud or sand during the day, and at night they emerge to find food using their senses of smell and touch. Some species will attempt to find live prey to which they attach themselves as parasites—they do this using specialised suckers, and once attached they rasp through the victim's skin and suck out its blood.

The Red Sea has some of the most colorful reefs in the world—here shoals of small orange fish swim past large pink corals.

Other species can travel long distances in order to seek out rotting food on which they can scavenge.

The jawed fishes are normally divided into three groups, these are the Chondrichthyes or rays, sharks and their relatives; the Osteichthyes or bony fish; and the Actinopterygii or ray-finned fishes. The chondrichthyes are similar to the rest of the vertebrate world in that they have functional jaws, and along with the bony fish and ray-finned fish have paired fins. They also have an endoskeleton that is entirely cartilaginous, and have no swim bladder or lung. This means that they have no natural buoyancy and have to keep swimming to stop themselves sinking. There are around 200 species of sharks, and about 350 species of skates and rays

alive today. Sharks are very good swimmers—the blue shark can reach speeds of nearly 45mph (70kph). While most sharks live in the open oceans, a few species live in freshwater rivers.

Nearly all sharks are predators, but only a few species have been known to attack man. The sharks and rays differ from the bony fish in that they have a powerful electro-receptive system, which can detect prey species in complete darkness. They can also track down their prey with an excellent sense of smell, as well as with superb sight and hearing. The bigger sharks may eat birds, seals, turtles as well as all manner of other fish. Penguins are a favourite prey of some of the cold water sharks; however, the two biggest species—the whale shark and basking

This shoal of yellowtop fuseliers (*Caesio xanthonota*) which come from the waters around the Surin Islands off Thailand, have been caught in a fisherman's net.

shark—feed exclusively on plankton. Sharks can also vary enormously in size: the smallest are the tiny pygmy sharks which only grow to 10in (250mm) long, but the largest of all fish is the whale shark, which can weigh up to 14 tons and grow to over 40ft (12m) in length. The skates and rays are generally similar to the sharks, but have flattened bodies with wing-like pectoral fins attached to the sides of the head.

The osteichthyes or bony fish have several key characteristics: they have a bony skeleton with numerous vertebrae; they usually have teeth; most have a swim bladder; and most lay eggs which are released into the water and fertilised externally.

The fish that most of us will be familiar with are the teleosts—these are members of the diverse group of ray-finned fishes, and include virtually all of the world's important sport and commercial fishes. Several countries have large fishing industries, and so teleosts contribute significant sums to their economies. These include Britain, Canada, Russia, Japan and Peru, although over-fishing has caused a major decline in the numbers of many commercial fish species—it is a source of major concern, and massive efforts are being made to boost fish stocks. There are many fish farms around the world—this is a practice that has gone on for a long time: the Chinese, for example have been doing so for over two thousand years.

Some fish species are particularly valued in the commercial world, and as such come under intense pressure from fishermen. None is more threatened

Blue striped snapper (*Lutjanus Kasmira*)

than the sturgeon, from which caviar is taken. It used to occur in large numbers in the bigger rivers of southern Russia, but these areas are hard to police so even statutory protection has little meaning in practice. Sadly, the future for the sturgeon currently looks bleak. Certain shark species are also being threatened with extinction—they are prized for their fins which are made into shark's fin soup. This is particularly popular in the Far East, where many other rare fish also end up on the dinner table on a daily basis.

Fish are not just under threat from over-fishing: many species have become extinct in recent years due to the introduction of alien species. Sometimes this is deliberate—the Nile Perch, for instance, was released into the waters of Lake Victoria in Africa to help increase the yield of the local fisheries by reducing the numbers of small fish. It is a large predatory species which got out of control, resulting in something like 200 species of cichlid fish becoming extinct in a very small period of time. Not all introductions are deliberate—accidental releases sometimes happen. This can occur when floods wash through fish farms or private ponds and captive fish escape into the native environment. Other human activities can also threaten fish species with extinction—large-scale engineering projects such as the construction of dams can have a catastrophic effect on the sustainability of some of the rarer species.

A shoal of Californian salema (*Xenistius californiensis*) swimming near Catalina Island.

FEEDING METHODS

The seas and oceans of the world are inhabited by an amazing array of fish species. This section examines some of the different ways in which they feed. The wolf fish, for instance, is a bottom feeder which seeks out hard-shelled invertebrates such as crabs: it then uses its powerful jaws to break through its prey's defensive armour. The giant moray has a completely different way of obtaining its food—It lurks in dark holes waiting for fish to swim past. When a suitable victim approaches, it darts out and grabs the unfortunate individual and then retreats back into the shadows. The ocean sunfish has evolved to filter large quantities of minute marine organisms from water which passes through its large mouth. The blue ribbon eel is a small member of the moray eel family; it lives in holes on the sea bed, from which it rises to snatch small animals as they pass. The gurnard and sturgeon are both bottom feeders, which use special feelers on their chins called barbels to find worms and other small creatures. Most of the quirky puffer fish family feed on hard-shelled invertebrates. The triggerfish are unlike the other fish described here because they are generalists, and will take more or less anything they can find, from algae, to sea urchins, to fish.

The wolf fish (*Anarhichas lupus*) is a member of the blenny family which inhabits rocky bottoms, where it feeds on hard-shelled molluscs, crabs, lobsters and sea urchins.

SNOWFLAKE MORAY EEL

Snowflake moray (*Echidna Nebulosa*), looking out of hidey hole in a colorful reef.

Ocean Sunfish

The ocean sunfish (*Mola mola*) is a filter feeder which swims in the open oceans of the world—the species has a dorsal fin which is sometimes mistaken for that of a shark.

PUFFER FISH

Some puffer fish species can grow up to 3ft (90cm) long. When attacked, these incredible animals not only inflate their bodies, but also erect special spines to defend themselves.

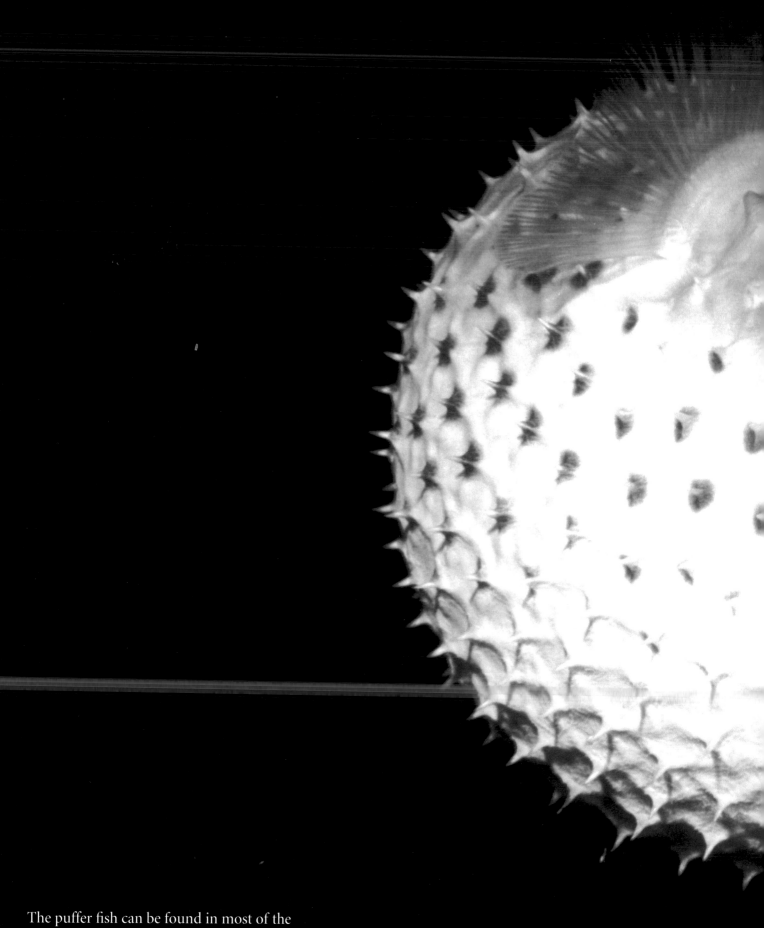

The puffer fish can be found in most of the
warmer seas of the world—this example, which
has inflated itself with air to scare off predators, is
from the Red Sea.

The shovelnose sturgeon (*Acipenser sturio*) is critically endangered—this is mostly due to the level of poaching in its native rivers.

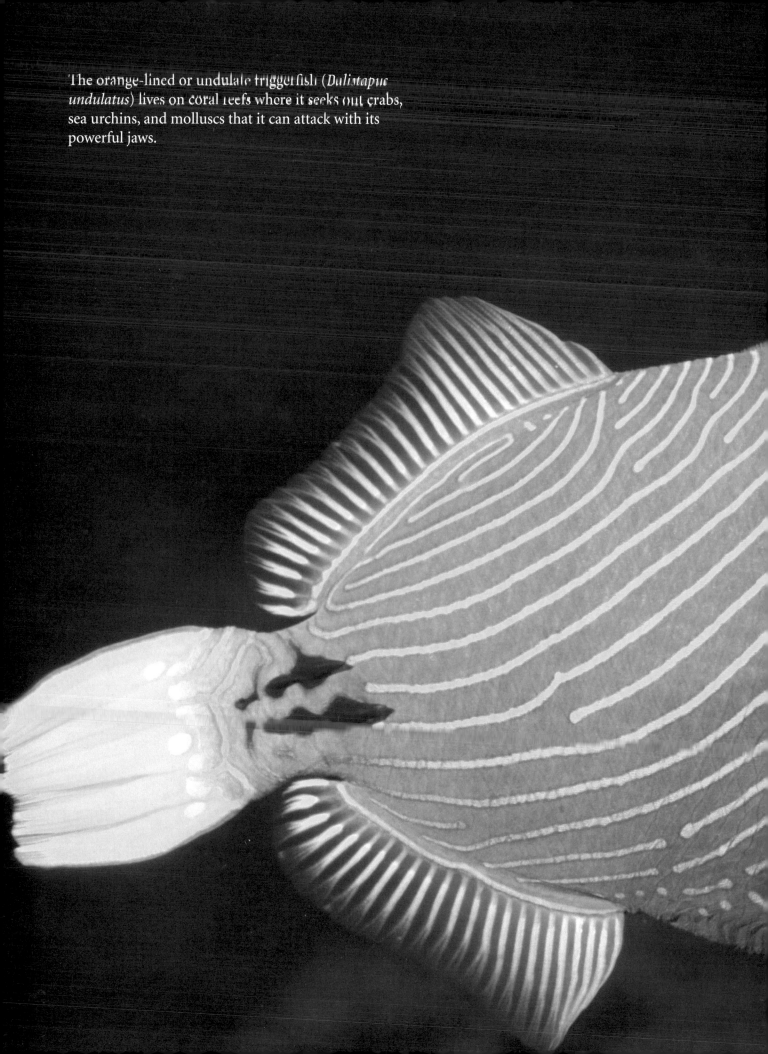

The orange-lined or undulate triggerfish (*Balistapus undulatus*) lives on coral reefs where it seeks out crabs, sea urchins, and molluscs that it can attack with its powerful jaws.

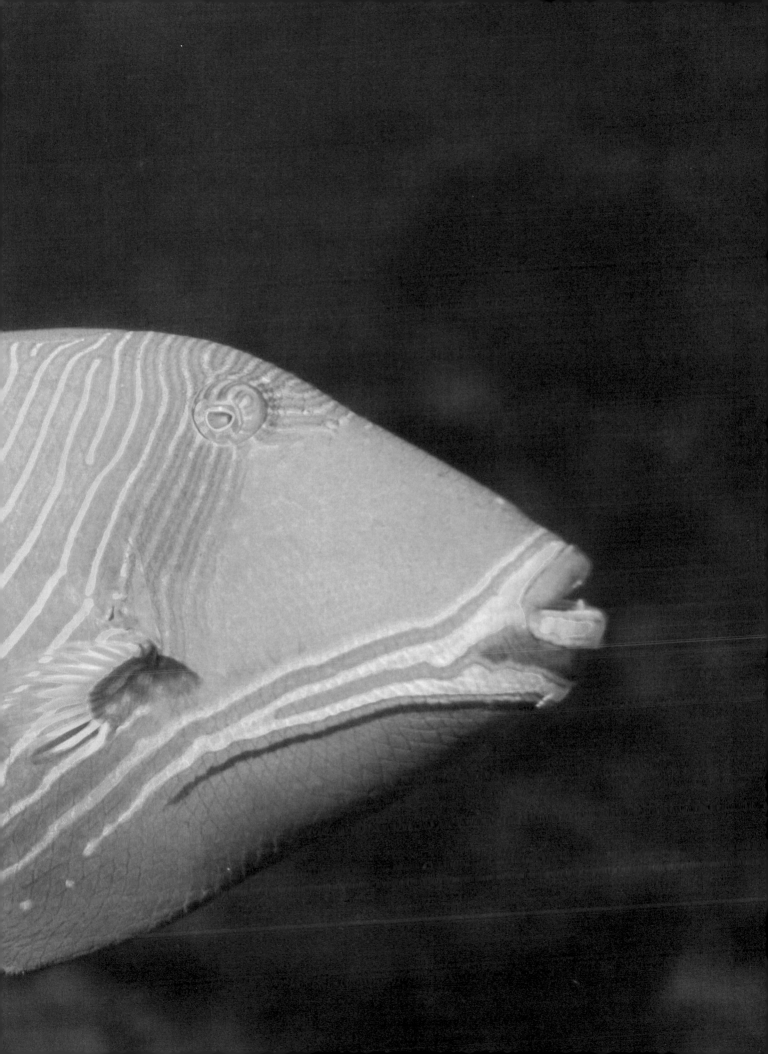

SHOAL & REEF FISH

For many animals there is strength in numbers, and fish are no exception. There are many hungry predators in the seas and oceans of the world, and for small species like the striped eel catfish, the odds of surviving an encounter with one of these improves as part of a shoal. Conversely, there are predators that like to hunt in aggressive packs—this is typified by the barracuda. These fast-swimming fish have mouths packed with sharp teeth, and when a group of them attack a reef it must be terrifying for the occupants. Reefs may be composed of stone or coral—both are often teeming with fish, and there are thousands of fish species which can live there and nowhere else. This section presents a series of different fish—those that shoal together and those that live on reefs; some, such as the blacksmith, do both.

The striped eel catfish (*Plotosus lineatus*) is found in the Red Sea where it often forms dense shoals. It is the only catfish found on coral reefs.

BLACKFIN BARRACUDA

Blackfin barracuda (*Sphyraena qenie*) are usually found in large schools near current-swept lagoons and seaward reefs where they are voracious predators.

The pymgy sweeper (*Parapriacanthus ransonneti*) can be found in large groups under coral and in caves during the day, but at night they venture out and feed on zooplankton.

The blacksmith (*Chromis punctipinnis*) is a small subtropical reef-dwelling fish that grows to a maximum of 10in (25cm) long.

The big-eye or marine soldier fish (*Myripristis murdjan*) is so named due to the fact that it has big eyes and gathers in large military-style formations.

CORAL GROUPER

The coral grouper (*Cephalopholis miniata*) lives in the dark nooks and crannies found on coral reefs, occasionally venturing forth to chase prey.

MEXICO SHEEPHEAD
The California or Mexico sheephead (*Semicossyphus pulcher*) grows up to 35lb (16kg) and 3ft (90cm) long. It prefers rocky places, particularly those with kelp beds.

BLOTCHEYE SOLDIERFISH AND CLEANER WRASSE

The cleaner wrasse (*Labroides dimidiatus*) specialises in removing parasites from other fish—here one can be seen above a blotcheye soldierfish (*Myripristis murdjan*).

CRESCENT-TAIL BIGEYE

The crescent-tail bigeye, or moontail bullseye (*Priacanthus hamrur*), is an uncommon species which feeds on small fish, crustaceans, and other small invertebrates.

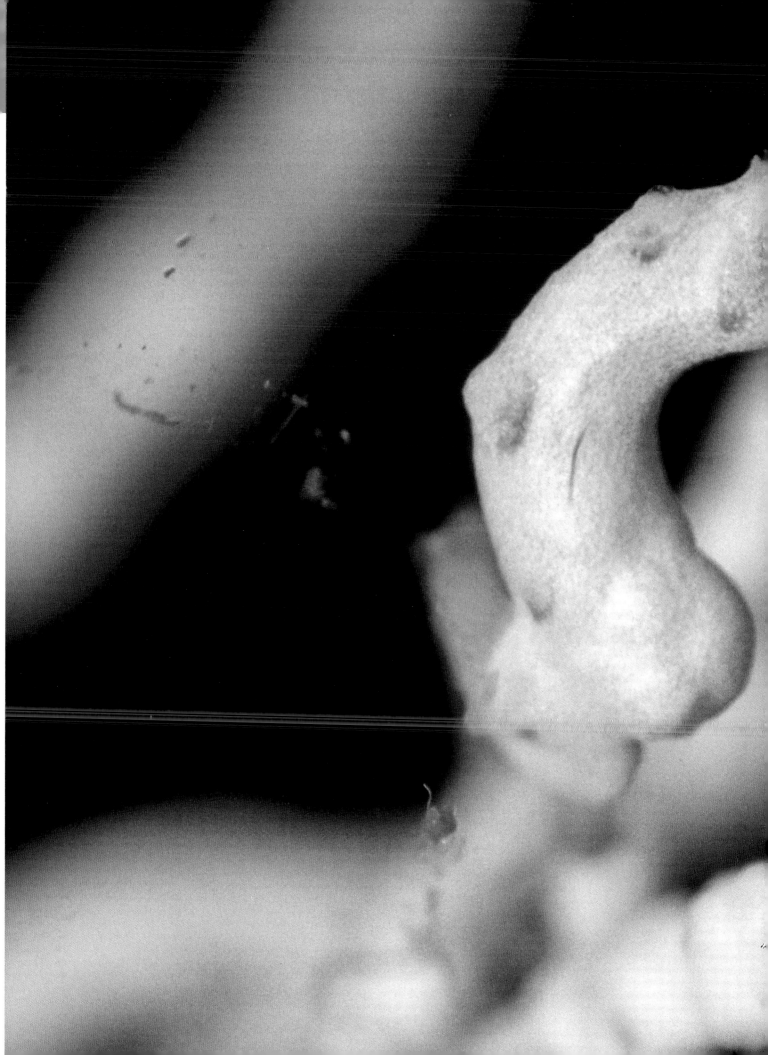

The pygmy seahorse (*Hippocampus bargibanti*) grows to 0.8in (2cm) in length and is remarkably well camouflaged, with its markings and coloration matching the soft corals it inhabits.

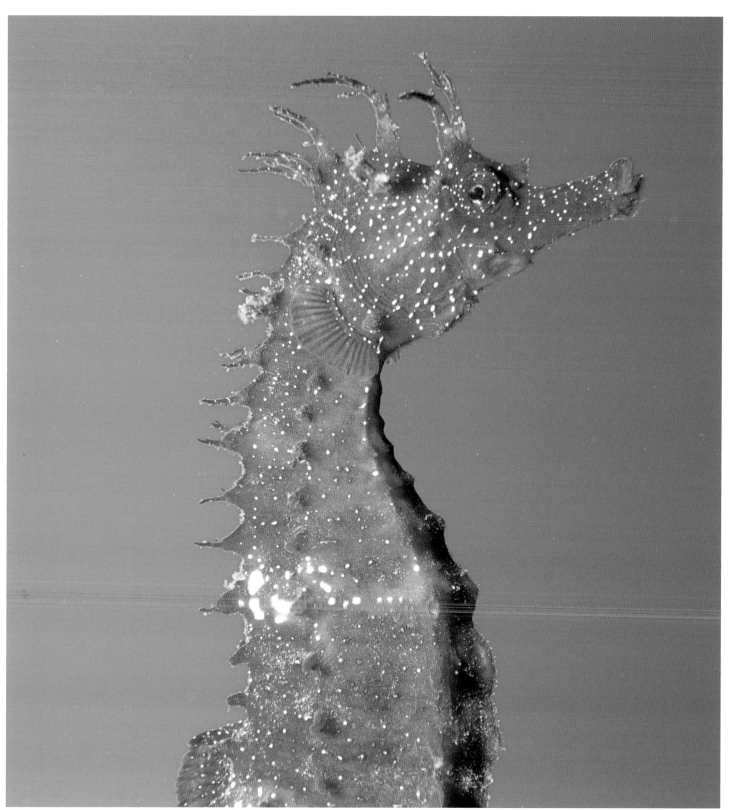

COMMON SEAHORSE

The common seahorse (*Hippocampus guttulatus*) lives in the Mediterranean and warm parts of the Atlantic. It swims upright using special fins to move through the water.

PYGMY SEAHORSE

The pygmy seahorse is so well camouflaged against pink corals that it was unknown to science until comparatively recently.

There are about 35 different species of seahorses, all of which are in the genus Hippocampus. Most spend the majority of their time hidden amongst seaweed or coral.

Lionfish & Zebrafish

The lionfish and zebrafish are spectacular creatures covered in dramatic stripes and equipped with long poison-tipped spines. They have been known to science for at least 250 years, and since then have become popular with the pet trade. They have many other common names, the commonest of which are 'turkeyfish' and 'firefish'. They are usually inhabitants of tropical reefs where they tend to hide up under rock ledges during the day. At night they often assemble in small shoals to cruise the reefs; however, they sometimes also venture close to beaches or enter estuaries.

This coral reef off the coast of Mauritius is alive with color and life, and there is no shortage of food for this lionfish (*Pterois volitans*) to eat.

ZEBRA LIONFISH

The various species of lionfish all have venomous spines and are usually found under ledges and in holes. This example is a zebra lionfish which feeds on small crustaceans.

LIONFISH

When lionfish get together in packs to go hunting, their fearsome toxic defences mean they have very little to fear in the way of predators.

SPOTFIN LIONFISH

The dramatic spotfin lionfish (*Pterois antennata*) is Guam's most common lionfish—it inhabits reefs and lagoons where it occurs singly or in small groups.

IDOLS & BUTTERFLYFISH

The Moorish idols and butterflyfish are ornate tropical fish which live in the lagoons and on the reefs of the tropical Indo-Pacific regions. They tend to have narrow, but tall bodies with colourful markings and long thin snouts. They use these delicate mouthparts to browse on algae, and more especially, sponges, as well as for catching small crustaceans, such as shrimps. They generally feed by day, and hide up under rocks and in narrow gullies by night to avoid predators. The idols and butterflyfish are not particularly big fish—they grow to a maximum of about 10in (25cm) long.

The Moorish idol (*Zanclus cornutus*) is a very striking fish which lives in the tropical seas near the Similan islands, off Thailand.

MASKED BANNERFISH

The spectacular masked bannerfish can be found in large numbers frequenting the shallow waters around the Maldive Islands in the Indian Ocean.

Garibaldi (*Hypsypops Rubicundus*) Coronado
Islands Mexico

'The Oriental sweetlips (*Plectorhinchus vittatus*) inhabits reefs and rocky areas in the shallower regions of the Indian ocean and grows to about 2 feet (60cm) in length.

RAYS

There can be few sights as impressive as a giant manta ray swooping majestically down over a tropical coral reef. Most of the members of this extensive group are, however, far less impressive. The majority of rays are bottom feeders, preying on things like crabs, molluscs, shrimps and small fish. They are often very well camouflaged, with patterns and colours which make them blend in with the sea bed so that they can avoid predators. Some, like the thornback ray are equipped with sharp spines, whereas other species like the stingray have poisonous stings in their tails to defend themselves.

The giant manta ray (*Manta birostris*) is like the sharks in that it is a cartilaginous fish. The remoras attached to its underside are, however, bony fish.

MOBULA RAY

There are several species of the spectacular mobula rays (*Mobula sp.*)—they can be found in tropical seas across the world where they feed at depths of up to 330ft (100m).

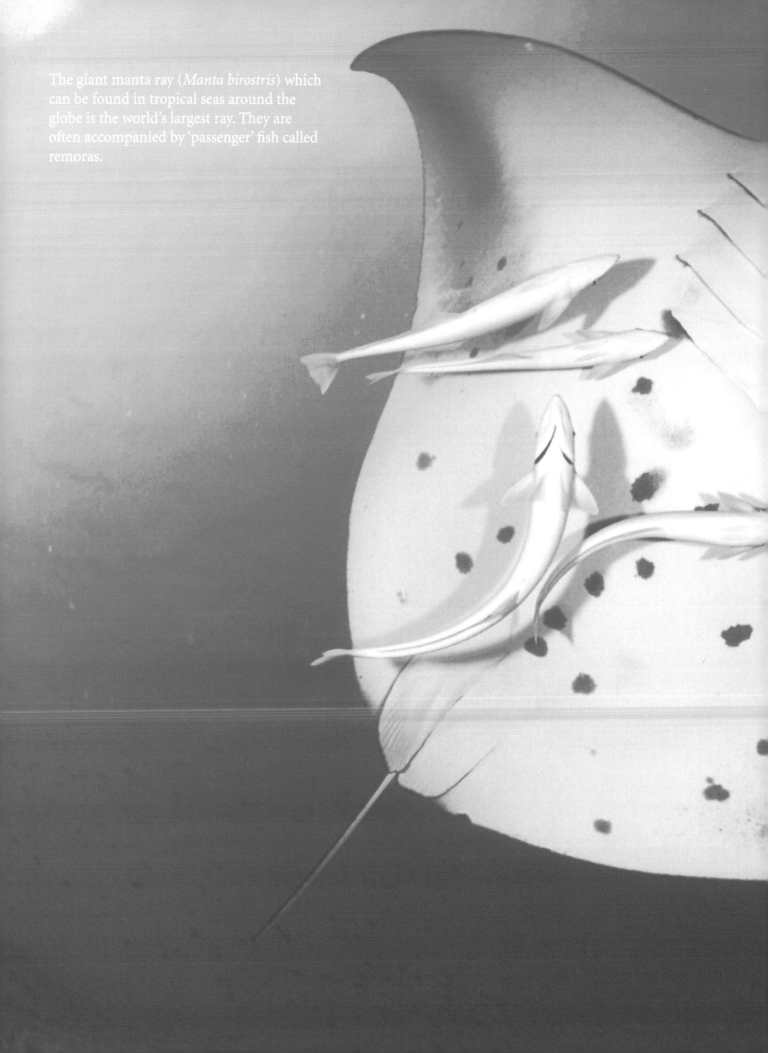

The giant manta ray (*Manta birostris*) which can be found in tropical seas around the globe is the world's largest ray. They are often accompanied by 'passenger' fish called remoras.

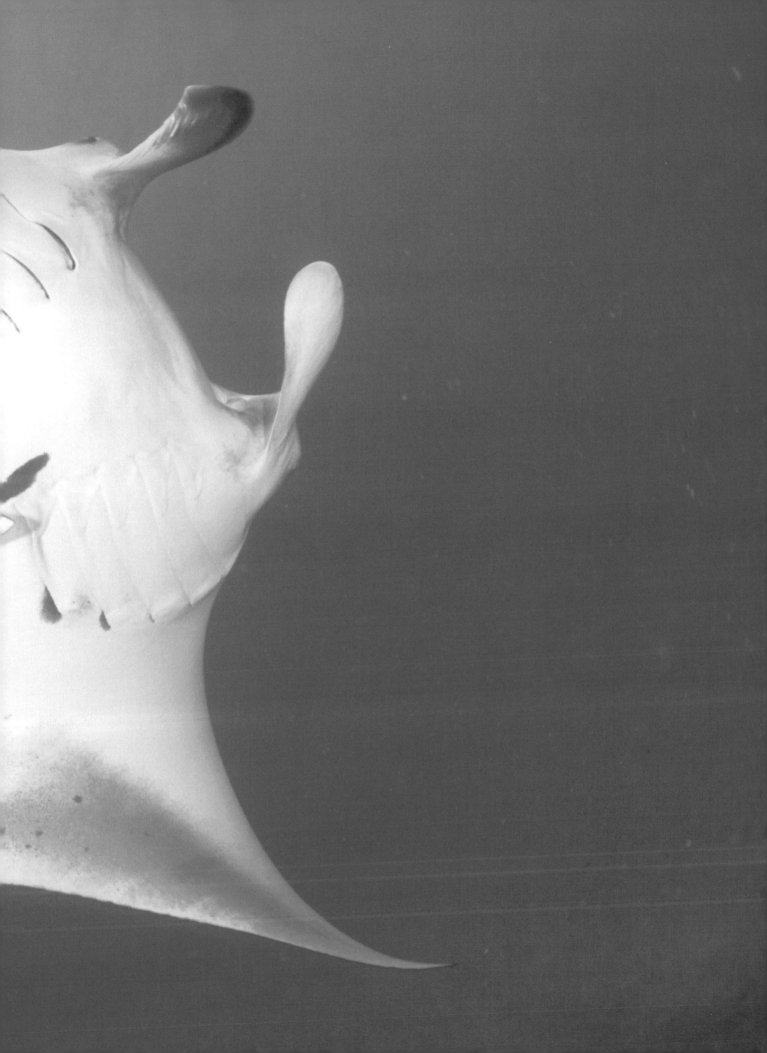

STINGRAY

Stingrays—as the name would suggest, possess the ability to administer a powerful acting. Consequently, they have very little to fear, and will allow divers to get very close.

Stingray

There are many different species of stingrays (*Taeniura sp.*)—this one has become used to being fed by fascinated divers.

CALIFORNIAN BAT RAY
A californian bat ray (*Myliobatis Californica*) glides amongst a forest of brown alga seaweed.

BLACK-SPOTTED STINGRAY

The black-spotted stingray lives in the coastal waters of the northern tropics—it is not usually aggressive, but at least one human death has been attributed to this fish.

SPOTTED EAGLE RAY

The spotted eagle ray (*Aetobatus narinari*) has an incredibly long tail and a large wingspan.

TORPEDO RAY

The Pacific electric or torpedo ray (*Torpedo californica*) occurs in the northeastern Pacific Ocean between Magdalena Bay, California (U.S.) to northern British Colombia (Canada).

SHARKS

The sharks are fish that frighten and fascinate us at the same time. The two biggest fish in the world are sharks—they are the aptly named whale shark, and the basking shark. These massive creatures are, however, completely harmless as they feed entirely on microscopic marine organisms called plankton. Other members of this group can be exceedingly dangerous though. The great white shark of Jaws fame is the most famous of the so-called killer species. The number of human deaths attributed to this awesome animal pales into insignificance though, when compared to, say, the number of deaths caused by bee stings each year. Most of the many shark species do not attack mankind, and do their best to stay out of the way should they ever encounter.

The crested horn shark (*Heterodontus galeatus*) lives on or near marine reefs—this example is eating the egg case of a Port Jackson shark (*Heterodontus portusjacksoni*).

CARIBBEAN REEF SHARK

The Caribbean reef shark (*Carcharhinus perezi*) is the most common shark on or around the coral reefs of the Caribbean.

The gray reef shark is a voracious predator that often assembles in large schools which scour nearby reefs for prey animals.

The whale shark (*Rhincodon typus*) is the largest fish in the world—it has a widespread distribution, occurring in all the tropical and warm seas, except the Mediterranean.

The leopard shark (*Stegostoma fasciatum*) is a slow-swimming fish which is able to work its way into narrow cracks and crevices in reefs to find food.

SAND TIGER SHARK

The sand tiger shark (*Carcharius taurus*) is also known as the gray nurse shark. It has a series of sharp, jagged teeth which it uses to capture small to medium sized fish.

SHARKS

SCALLOPED HAMMERHEAD SHARK

The scalloped hammerhead shark (*Sphyrna lewini*) has excellent vision which is helped by having its eyes positioned at each end of its hammer shaped head.

The hammerhead shark is a fearsome predator which has a strangely shaped head—this contains special sensory organ which help it track down its prey.

CLOWNFISH & ANEMONEFISH

The clownfish and anemonefishes are well known for living in what would seem to be the very jaws of death, for they spend most of their lives between the tentacles of large sea anemones. If any other kind of fish were to venture into the clutches of the anemone in the same way, it would surely be killed. This strange situation is easily explained, however, since the anemonefish guards its host, chasing away things like butterflyfish which often attack and eat tropical anemones. They also make sure that no parasites manage to get close enough to cause injury. In return, the anemone protects the fish—this arrangement is an excellent example of mutual symbiosis. The fish itself is protected from the anemone's stings by a special mucous.

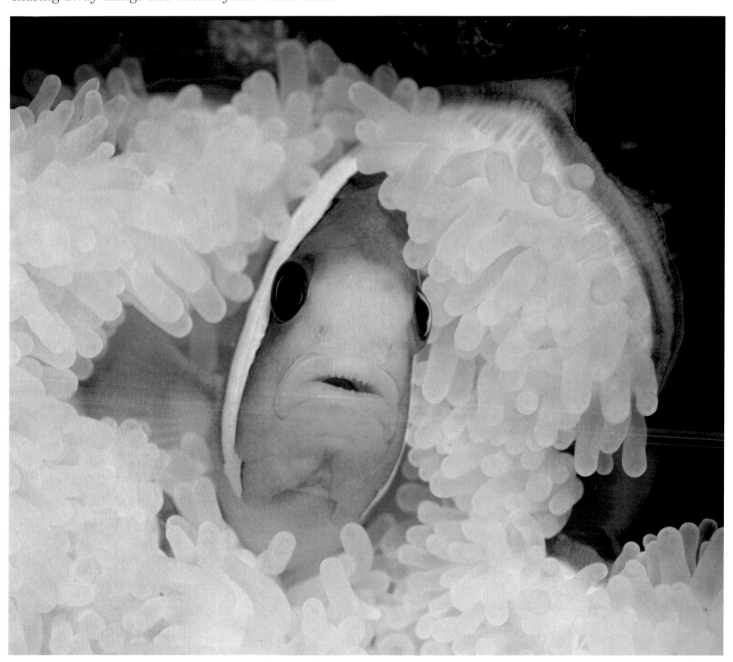

The Malayasian clownfish has a close association with certain anemone species—in return for protection these small fish keep harmful pests away from their well-armed hosts.

OMAN ANEMONEFISH

This orange fish with its white stripes is a juvenile Oman anemonefish (*Amphiprion omanensis*). It occurs in the waters of the western Indian Ocean.

CLARK'S ANEMONEFISH

The Clark's anemonefish (*Amphiprion clarkii*) is charcterised by its yellow body and blue stripes. It inhabits lagoons and outer reef slopes.

ORANGE FIN ANEMONE FISH

The orange fin anemone fish (*Amphiprion chrysopterus*) inhabits shallow seas and calm lagoons—it has a symbiotic relationship with several species of sea anemones.

Pink Anemonefish

The pink anemonefish (*Amphiprion perideraion*) hides amongst the poisonous stinging tentacles of anemones, from where it occasionally makes brief forays to find food.

KIRIBATI SPINECHEEK ANEMONEFISH

The Kiribati spinecheek anemonefish (*Premnas biaculeatus*) is usually found in pairs—the males tend to be much smaller than the females.

SCORPIONFISH, ANGLERFISH & FROGFISH

The fish presented in this section are all species that spend much of their time pretending to be rocks or other solid objects. The scorpionfish is also often called the stonefish—either way it is a very dangerous creature which inflicts painful injuries, some of which can be fatal, on many holidaymakers every year. This is because it lies on the seabed in shallow water, where it partially buries itself so that only its poisonous spines are showing through. Although it is only waiting to catch passing shrimps or small fish, it can't be seen by the casual human observer, who,

if stung, will need immediate medical treatment. The anglerfish, however, is not hazardous to humans, although to small animals it is deadly. It gets its name from the fact that it has a special structure which is shaped to look like a worm—it waves this whenever a suitable prey species is nearby, and if the intended victim swims closer to have a look, the anglerfish will dart forward and consume it.

The tassled scorpionfish (*Scorpaenopsis oxycephala*) is protected by venomous spines and inhabits clear-water reefs and channels where it lies on the sea bed waiting for prey.

MERLET'S SCORPIONFISH

Merlet's scorpionfish (*Rhinopias aphanes*) is a rare species that inhabits coral slopes, or soft bottom habitat. It grows to a maximum size of 10in (25cm).

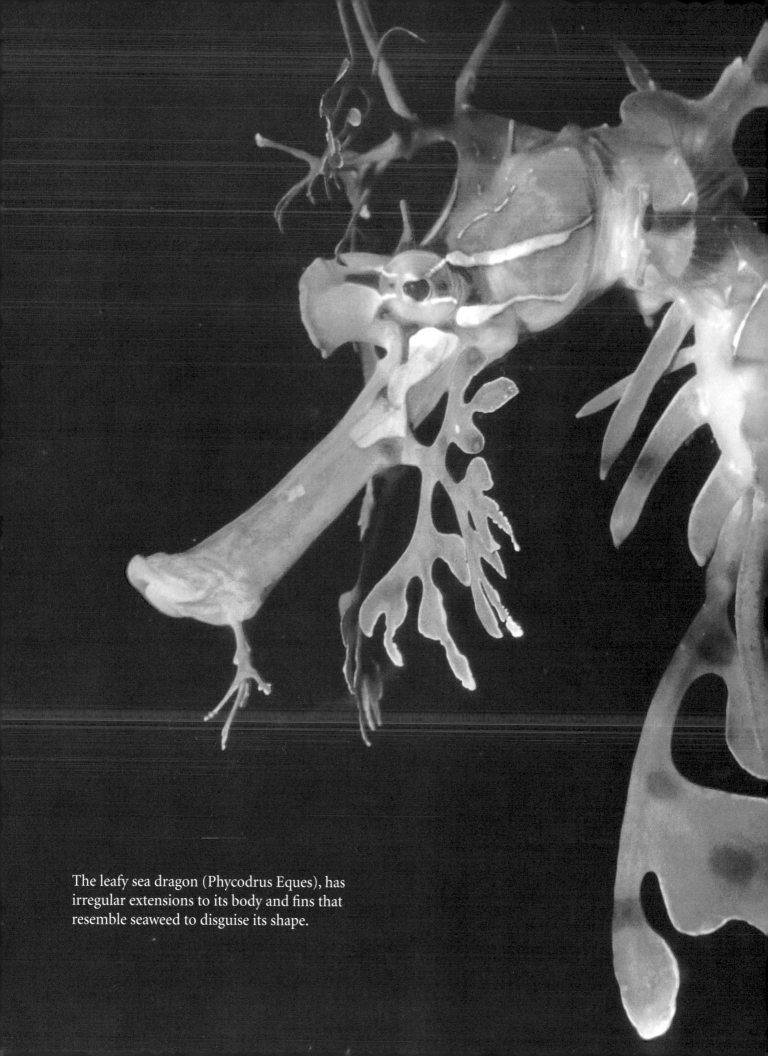

The leafy sea dragon (Phycodrus Eques), has irregular extensions to its body and fins that resemble seaweed to disguise its shape.

INDONESIAN LEAF FISH

The Indonesian leaf fish (*Taenianotus trianthus*) is particularly adept at camouflaging itself amongst coral where it avoids predators and awaits prey.

SARGASSUM ANGLERFISH

The Sargassum anglerfish (*Histrio histrio*) swims under mats of floating seaweed—has very effective camouflage which it uses to evade predators.

LACY SCORPIONFISH
The Lacy scorpionfish (*Rhinopius aphanes*) has blackened body camouflage to help it merge in with the background.
It inhabits reefs and rocky ground in the waters around Papua New Guinea.

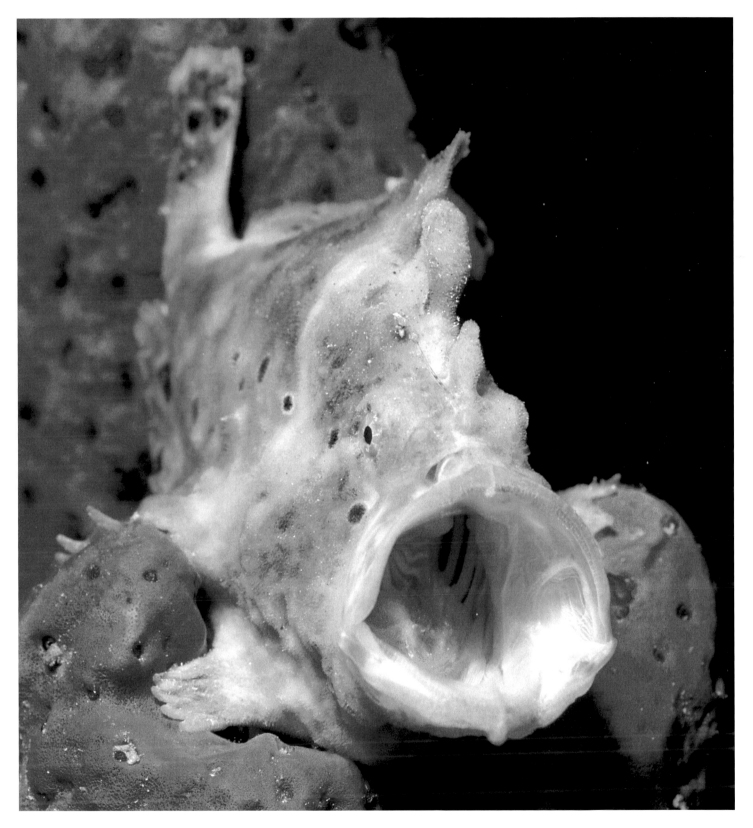

LONGLURE FROGFISH

The longlure frogfish (*Antennarius multiocellatus*) uses a small appendage which works as a lure to entice small fish or crustaceans towards its cavernous mouth.

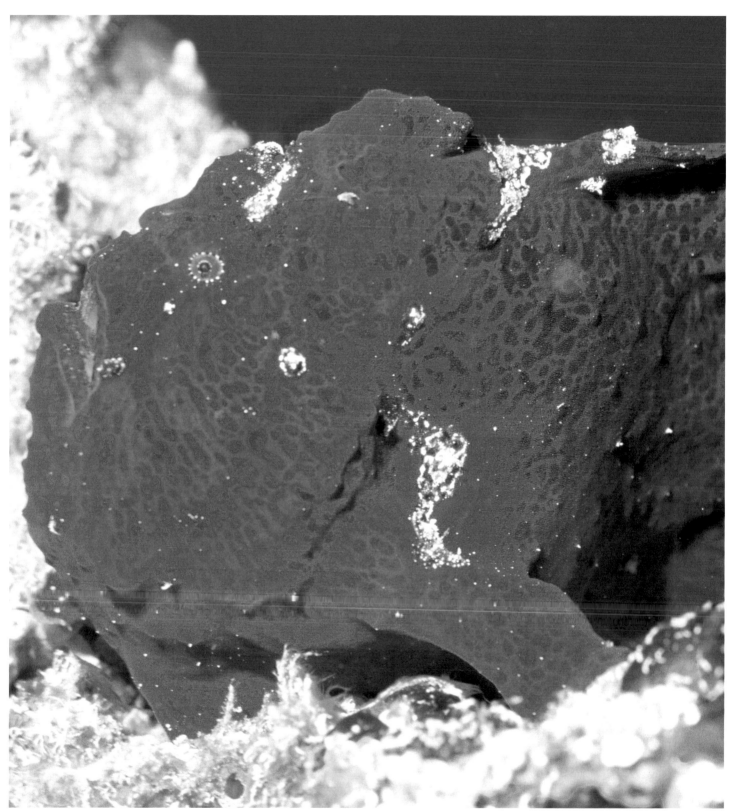

Commerson's Frogfish

Many fish found on coral reefs have vivid colors and highly unusual shapes, this example is called Commerson's frogfish (*Antennarius commersoni*).

COMMERSON'S FROGFISH

Commerson's frogfish uses its irregular-shaped body for camouflage and uses a lure that mimics small worms to attract small fish which it then eats.

CALEDONIAN STINGER

The Caledonian stinger or Chinese ghoul (*Inimicus caledonicus*) is a venomous member of the stonefish family with a superbly camouflaged body.

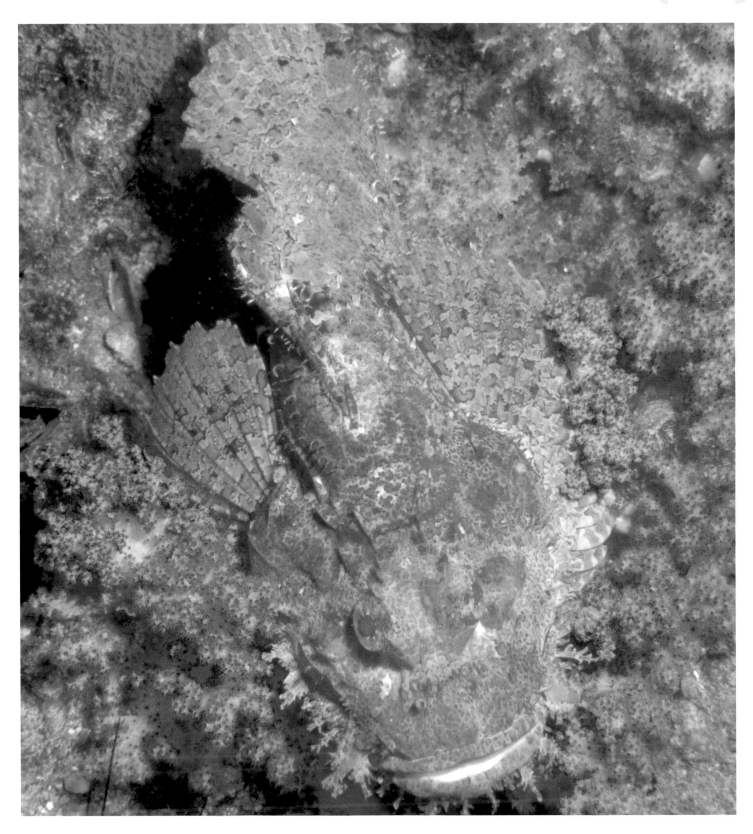

SCORPION FISH

This scorpion fish is using its natural camouflage to hide among the rocks.

Birds belong to the class Aves, and are the only animals that have feathers. They also have other common characteristics: they are all vertebrates; they have forclimbs which arc modified into wings; they have no teeth; they have scales on their feet; they lay eggs; and they are all warm-blooded. The current scientific opinion is that birds evolved from a common reptile ancestor. When the first fossil Archaeopteryx was discovered, it was found that it had feathers—this was the first proof that birds had existed since such early times. These first primitive birds evolved more than 150 million years ago. No other animal has feathers—they are unique to birds, and originally evolved from the scales of their common reptilian ancestor. Feathers are very light, and are made of a strong protein called keratin—the same material that is used in mammalian hair and fingernails.

Although all birds have feathers, not all of them can fly. Many have evolved to fill specialised ecological roles and as such have lost the power of flight. Some of these, such as the dodo, did not need to fly as they had no natural predators on the remote islands where they lived. Tragically, many became extinct as soon as seafarers introduced alien species such as rats, goats and deer. Feathers are not just used for flight, however, they are often coloured or patterned for particular purposes. This may be for social or courtship purposes, or it may be to provide camouflage to avoid predators finding

Seagulls taking advantage of the opportunity to scavenge at a landfill site.

BIRDS – CLASS *AVES*

them. In the case of birds which live in harsh arctic environments—like the penguins, feathers are used to act as a vital insulation barrier against the cold. Swimming birds like the penguins also use their feathers to keep them dry—they use oils secreted from special glands to create a kind of water-proofing agent.

Birds show their reptilian ancestry in another way too: they all hatch from eggs which are laid outside the body. These all have hard shells and contain large yolks. While not all reptiles foster their young, all birds need a considerable amount of care after they have hatched. Some species, like the cuckoo cheat by laying their eggs in the nests of other species. They then leave their young to be brought up by the nest's often bewildered owners—it is not at all uncommon for the cuckoo chicks to be larger than both the foster parents combined!

There are about 30 orders of birds in all—these are split across about 180 families, and are subdivided into about 2,000 genera with 10,000 individual species. There are many more subspecies, but a lot of these are still the subject of scientific dispute, as their defining characters have yet to be established.

Almost every possible food source is exploited by birds—what a bird eats can usually be deduced from the sizes and shapes of its beak and feet. Species with long thin beaks usually either specialise in sipping nectar from flowers—this includes the well-known hummingbirds, or those which seek out insects and

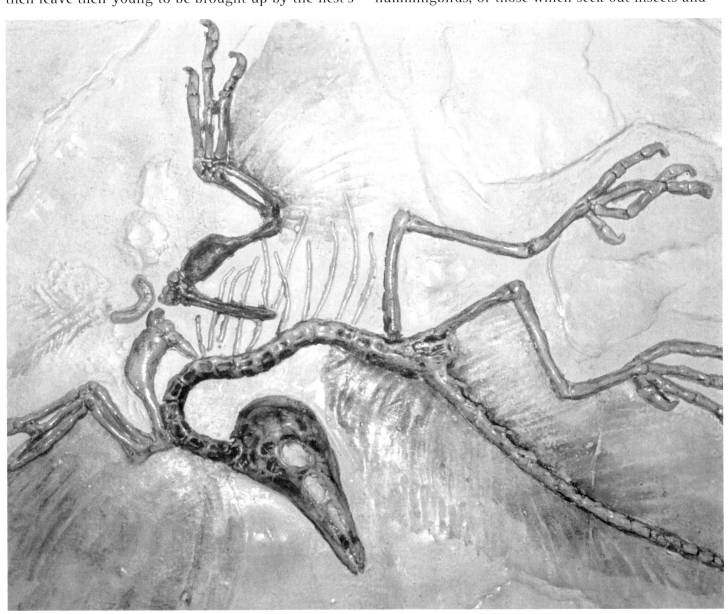

The Archaeopteryx was one of the earliest birds—this fossil was the first evidence that such creatures had feathers.

IBIS, HERONS, EGRETS & CRANES

The birds covered in this section all have a very similar and distinctive profile: they have long legs, a sleek body, a long neck and a long beak. They have these similarities because they all fill a similar ecological niche—that is, they all feed in open areas such as meadows and alongside waterways. The scarlet ibis, for instance, feeds on shrimps in shallow estuarine and coastal waters; it is from the crustaceans that these beautiful birds get their bright red coloration. Herons, however, wait patiently by bodies of water for small fish or amphibians to swim by: they then pluck their victims from the water and consume them. Egrets and storks, on the other hand, will take both fish and crustaceans, and larger species like the great egret will also take small mammals if they get the chance. The crane usually feeds on land, eating seeds, grain, and is especially fond of acorns.

The scarlet ibis (*Eudocimus ruber*) is a bright red bird which feeds in groups on the marshes and mangrove swamps of northern South America and down as far as eastern Brazil.

Gray Heron

The gray heron (*Ardea cinerea*) can be found fishing in shallow waters from Africa, through Europe and across Asia as far as Japan.

The green-backed or striated heron (*Butorides striatus*) is distributed across the tropical and subtropical regions of the Americas, Africa, and Asia.

YELLOW-BILLED STORK

The Yellow-billed Stork, (*Mycteria ibis*) is an African bird that hunts for small aquatic animals by flushing them out of the mud with one foot and catching them as they try to swim off.

Great White Egret

The common or great white egret (*Ardea alba*, formerly *Casmerodius albus*) was very nearly made extinct by the trade in their feathers for the fashion industry.

The reddish egret (*Egretta rufescens*) is an inhabitant of shallow bays, lagoons and mangrove swamps along the Gulf coastline of Texas, Louisiana, and Mexico as well as the Caribbean.

The wood duck (*Aix sponsa*) is considered by many to be the most colorful waterfowl species in North America.

MALLARD
The mallard (*Anas platyrhynchos*) prefers to inhabit wetland areas where it can find the vegetation, insects, worms, and arthropods on which it normally feeds.

MANDARIN CHICK

The mandarin duck (*Aix galericulata*) lives in the forests of China and Japan where its diet consists of water plants, as well as rice and other grains.

The Hawaiian goose or 'Ne Ne' (*Branta sandvicensis*) came close to extinction, but captive breeding saved the species—this is an excellent example of a conservation success.

The red-throated diver (*Gavia stellata*) is a species which breeds in the far north of both Eurasia and North America.

There are two races of the white-fronted goose (*Anser albifrons*)—one lives in Siberia, and the other in Greenland. Both feed on grass, clover, grain, winter wheat and potatoes.

BIRDS - CLASS *AVES*

LONG-LEGGED WADERS

There can be few sights as spectacular as a colony of flamingos, with their bright pink plumage. Like the ibises, these magnificent birds get their unusual coloration from pigments contained in their diet. This consists of certain small shrimp species—when they are kept in captivity, flamingos will turn white unless special additives are mixed in with their food. Avocets have distinctive beaks: unusually, they are curled upwards. This is because they have adapted to make use of a very specialised feeding technique.

They hunt for small crustaceans at the edges of rivers and estuaries, where they put their heads forward and move their beaks from side to side through the soft mud. The spoonbill uses a similar method, but goes for a slightly different range of small creatures. While the aptly named long-billed curlew may be seen at the water's edge, it is primarily a bird of the open grassland, where it grazes on small invertebrates using its long thin beak.

The lesser flamingo (*Phoeniconaias minor*) lives in colonies—this one is on the edge of Lake Magadi in the Rift Valley of Kenya.

RED-NECKED AVOCET
The red-necked avocet (*Recurvirostra novaehollandiae*) has an upturned bill which is specialised for feeding on brine shrimp in the soft mud of inland estuaries and coastal salt marshes.

341

The long-billed curlew (*Numenius americanus*) was once very common on the prairies, but habitat loss and over-hunting have caused its numbers to decline dramatically.

ROSEATE SPOONBILL

The roseate spoonbill (*Ajaia ajaja*) inhabits areas heavily populated with mangroves where the nutrient rich water is teeming with small fish, crustaceans and insects.

Hawaiian Stilt

The Hawaiian Stilt, (*Himantopus mexicanus knudseni*) likes to feed on open mudflats or pastures where it can spot predators easily.

BIRDS - CLASS *AVES*

BIRDS OF SEA & SEASHORE

The seashore is an excellent place to observe all manner of birds. Sadly, it is also a place where many dead birds are washed up for all to see. When a pollution incident such as an oil spill occurs, effected birds will end up on the beach covered in oily residues. Some of the lucky ones will be rescued by volunteers before it is too late, but sadly, the vast majority die. Some birds like the albatross are rarely seen—this is because they spend most of their lives gliding over the southern oceans, and only go ashore on remote islands to breed. The seagulls are one group of birds that have, in the main, benefited from human activities. In the past they would only go inland when the sea was rough. Indeed, seeing gulls on farmland used to be a way of foretelling the weather. These days, however, refuse tips and landfill sites teem with thousands of hungry gulls all busy scavenging for the scraps that we have thrown away.

This juvenile brown booby (*Sula leucogaster*) was raised in the Rose Atoll National Wildlife Refuge in American Samoa.

BIRDS OF SEA & SEASHORE
ORDER *CHARADRIIFORMES*, *PROCELLARIIFORMES*, *PELECANIFORMES*

GREAT FRIGATE BIRD

The great frigate bird (*Fregata minor*) which is found on the Galapagos Islands has a ritualised courtship display—here the male can be seen inflating his large red throat sac.

347

The lesser black-backed gull (*Larus fuscus*) is only found in Europe where there is great concern for its long-term welfare—for unknown reasons its numbers are declining in many places.

GUILLEMOT

This common guillemot (*Uria aalge*) was a victim of a shipwreck on the Shetland Isles—the consequent oil spill killed thousands of seabirds and other animals.

PUFFIN

The puffin (*Fratercula arctica*) normally eats its catch underwater, however, when it is seen like this—with a beakful of sand eels, it is a clear indication that it has nestlings to feed.

WANDERING ALBATROSS

The wandering albatross (*Diomedea exulans*) is the largest member of the albatross family. They build their nests in extended colonies on flat grasslands.

BIRDS OF SEA & SEASHORE
ORDER *CHARADRIIFORMES, PROCELLARIIFORMES, PELECANIFORMES*

GANNET
The gannet (*Sula bassana*) is a majestic bird—when it soars like this it can cover great distances with very little effort.

When the gannet has reached its chosen fishing grounds, it hovers over the water waiting for the right moment to dive in and capture a fish.

LITTLE TERN

The little tern (*Sterna albifrons*) is a summer visitor to Europe, arriving in April and May. It spends the winter on the coasts of Africa.

OYSTERCATCHER

The Oystercatcher, (*Haematopus ostralegus*) is a distinctive bird that hunts for small invertebrates along the tidelines of estuaries and beaches.

COMMON TERN

The common tern has to guard its nest carefully—if they are given the chance, gulls and crows will steal unattended eggs very quickly.

BLUE-FOOTED BOOBIE

The blue-footed booby's (*Sula nebouxii*) range is restricted to the Galapagos Islands—the individual seen here is performing part of its mating ritual.

BROWN PELICAN

The brown pelican (*Pelecanus occidentalis californicus*) which is an expert fish-catcher is found on the west coasts of the United States and Mexico.

BROWN BOOBIE

The brown booby (*Sula leucogaster*) is a master of the air—it has a large wingspan, which it puts to good use in seeking out prey and carrion.

BIRDS - CLASS *AVES*

OWLS

Most owls are nocturnal hunters, a role for which they have some superb adaptations. They all have very large eyes; this allows them to capture as much light as possible so that they can see their prey on the darkest of nights. They also have feathers which produce very little noise in flight: this way owls can hover over small mammals without giving away their presence. Some owls specialise in hunting for very small prey; beetles and worms form the diet of a number of species. Other owls, however, will take much bigger prey: the eagle owls, for instance, will successfully hunt rabbits, hares and anything else of a similar they can find and kill. Their chief weapons are their talons—these tend to be very sharp and very strong. Although they also have powerful beaks, these are mainly used for cutting up their food. Unlike the majority of the others in this group, the snowy owl hunts by day. This is because it lives in the arctic wastes, where the summers are short, and it can be daylight right around the clock. Consequently, their prey tends to be active all the time, and the owls make the most of it while they can.

The great horned owl (*Bubo virginianus*) can be found throughout the United States and Canada, and as far south as the Straits of Magellan.

362

GREAT GRAY OWL

The great gray owl (*Strix nebulosa*) has exceptional hearing, and can detect a rodent moving under 12in (30cm) of snow.

Although the tawny owl (*Strix aluco*) is an accomplished hunter of rodents, it also eats large numbers of insects, earthworms and other small creatures.

SNOWY OWL

Unlike the majority of owls, the snowy owl (*Nyctea scandiaca*) hunts in daylight.

OTHER BIRDS OF PREY – ORDER *FALCONIFORMES*

OTHER BIRDS OF PREY

The birds of prey are many people's favourite species—indeed, so popular has it become that the bald eagle is now established as one of the main symbols of America as a nation. There are many other kinds of birds in this category too. At one end of the spectrum there is the kestrel: this is a small bird that hovers above the ground looking for small mammals or reptiles. At the other end there are the massive vultures, which soar above many of the wild places in the world looking for carrion on which they can scavenge. In between there are many medium-sized species, including the ospreys which are expert fisher catchers, and the goshawks which are the true masters of the air. Incredibly, these aerial acrobats are able to chase down prey birds at high speed through woods and forests without ever hitting anything solid.

There are 13 different species of kestrels—most of these hover above the ground before dropping onto their prey, which generally consists of small mammals, insects and reptiles.

An Osprey (*Pandion Haliaetus*) - flying back to its nest with food for its young.

STRIATED CARACARA

The main range of the striated caracara (*Phalcoboenus australis*) is the Falkland Islands. It is an endangered bird of prey which take other birds as well as carrion.

GOLDEN EAGLE

The golden eagle (*Aquila chrysaetos*) is the largest predatory bird in North America and northern Europe. The individual seen here is feeding on fresh kill in the Scottish Highlands.

The bald eagle (*Haliaeetus leucocephalus*) is seen as an American symbol. It has a powerful bill which it uses to consume fish as well as waterfowl, rabbits, muskrats and carrion.

The sparrow hawk (*Accipiter nisus*) is so named because it chases and catches small birds on the wing. Here an adult can be seen on its nest with several young.

The red-backed shrike (*Lanius collurio*) breeds on heaths and commons where there are thorn bushes. The female seen here has just delivered a large caterpillar to her nestlings.

Woodpigeon (*Columba palumbus*) is Europe's largest pigeon; the adults can be readily identified by the white patch on the side of the neck.

The secretary bird (*Sagittarius serpentarius*) is a long legged bird of prey which hunts for insects, lizards, snakes, tortoises and rats. Large prey are stamped to death and then eaten.

SOMALI OSTRICH

Ostrich feathers were once a favorite of the fashion industry, and this led to large numbers being hunted. This individual is using them for their intended purpose—for courtship rituals.

FOWL BIRDS - ORDER *GALLIFORMES*

FOWL BIRDS

There are many different kinds of birds which fall into this category—they range from the humble domestic hen to the ostentatious peacock. All the males have elegant plumage, whereas most of the females are drab in comparison. This is because the courtship rituals of wild fowl birds are extensive and complicated. Many, such as the capercaillie and the grouse, have communal parade grounds where the entire local population will gather to watch the males perform their dances. The females choose their mates based on what they observe—their judgements are based on the competence and vigour of the performance as well as the quality of the individual male's plumage. Both are good indicators of its health and status in the community. These factors are important for the long-term survival of the species, and so these dances are not the frivolous waste of time that they may appear to be.

The cockerel is a male domestic chicken (*Gallus domesticus*)—it has brightly colored feathers which it uses to impress the females.

Domestic Hen

This is a female domestic chicken—they have been bred to form many different varieties—this one is mainly Rhode Island Red.

OCELLATED TURKEY

The ocellated turkey (*Agriocharis ocellata*) can be found in the tropical forests of the Yucatan Peninsula of Mexico, as well as in Guatemala, and Belize.

The male peacock or common peafowl (*Pavo cristatus*) is highly visible, in contrast to the hen bird which is a drab brown color.

PEACOCK

When the male peacock wants to impress a hen bird, it raises its tail feathers in a fan shape, producing this spectacular display.

CAPERCAILLIE

Capercaillie (*Tetrao urogallus*) is a resident of pine forests in northern Europe and Asia. This male is performing a special display as part of its courtship rituals.

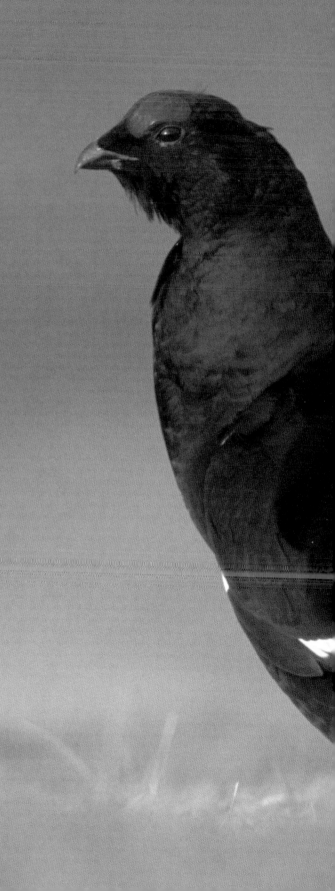

The black grouse (*Tetrao tetrix*) is another species
where the male displays at a communal site. These
beautiful black and white birds live in woodland and
scrub where heather is common.

VULTURINE GUINEA FOWL

The vulturine guinea fowl (*Acryllium vulturinum*) is a distinctive East African bird that perches on trees or posts to make loud territorial calls.

Parrots, Macaws & Cockatoos

The parrot family belongs to the order Psittaciformes and contains 328 different species. These can range in size from the pygmy parrots at only 3.6in (9cm) to the hyacinth macaw which can reach 40in (100cm) in height. Most of the South American species are various shades of green, however, others can be more or less any colour under the spectrum. They are primarily forest dwellers of the tropical and subtropical regions of the world, and most will eat seeds, fruit, nectar and pollen, although sometimes they will take insects or small animals. They can be incredibly long-lived: the smaller species will usually only survive between 10 and 15 years, but the larger ones such as the macaws and cockatoos can live to more than 75 years of age!

The Indian ring-necked parakeet (*Psittacula krameri manillensis*) is native to southern India and Sri Lanka, although it has been introduced to many other countries worldwide.

The sulphur crested cockatoo (*Cacatua galerita*) is distributed across Australia and New Guinea. When these birds assemble in large numbers they can be extremely noisy.

These red and green macaws (*Ara chloropterus*) have assembled at their nest colony which is on a cliff face well out of the way of most predators.

MACAW

Here, two different species of macaw are sitting alongside each other. On the left is the scarlet macaw (*Ara macao*), and on the right is the caninde macaw (*Caninde macao*).

NESTING

Building nests is an instinctive behaviour for most birds, although just how they inherit this knowledge is still a mystery. Some, like the cuckoos, simply hijack nests from other species, whereas others blatantly steal them by evicting the rightful owners and moving in. Some of the cliff dwelling sea birds don't make any attempt to build a nest: they just lay their eggs onto a narrow ledge and make do. Many birds, such as the skylark, will go to enormous lengths to disguise the whereabouts of their nest; however, species like the white stork could not make theirs more obvious.

While some birds barely make a nest at all, others go to an enormous amount of trouble to do so. This marvelous structure is that of the sunbird (*Nectarinia coccinigaster*).

DOVE

When a bird returns to its nest it needs superb control, or else it risks crushing its own young. This dove is demonstrating how the flight feathers help it land.

BILLS & PLUMAGE

Some birds are exquisitely beautiful—the birds of paradise being a good example; others, like the marabou stork, look like something out of a horror movie. There are all sorts of different ways that birds dress themselves up:some, like the peacock use elaborate feathers. Many others, however, have different solutions to the problem. The domestic cockerel, for instance, has a structure called a 'comb' on the top of its head—this is often coloured bright red to draw attention to it. The toucan combines fashion with function by having an enormous beak which is brightly coloured—it uses this as a tool to get at its food. Birds like the snipe need very delicate beaks so that they can accurately retrieve small invertebrates from the ground. The shoebill needs a beak that it can use to sieve tiny crustaceans from shallow water, whereas the parrot has to break open nuts and seeds. All in all, there are as many different kinds of beaks as there are ecological niches!

The blue and yellow macaw (*Ara ararauna*) has a diet which includes many hard-shelled nuts and seeds. In order to crack them open, it has a very powerful beak.

419

There are 37 species of toucans (*Toco sp*). They all have enormous bills which they use to break open nuts and seeds as well as to catch large insects.

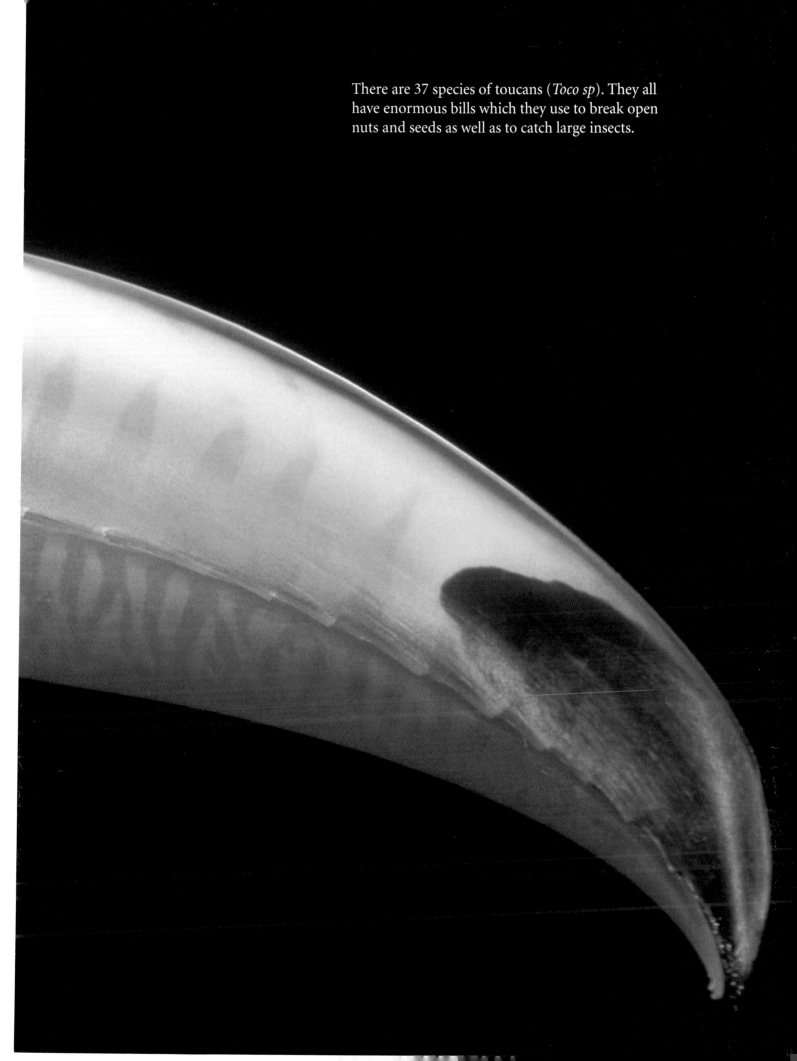

ROBIN

The robin (*Erithacus rubecula*) is well-known to all European residents. The male is very territorial, and will fight other males to the death if necessary to defend its patch.

FINCHES, LARKS & OTHER SMALL BIRDS
ORDER *PASSERIFORMES*

WAXWING
The waxwing (*Bombycilla garrulus*) is a small bird with a characteristic tuft of feathers on the top of its head.

The skylark (*Alauda arvensis*) is a bird of cultivated land, meadows and heathland areas. It ranges throughout Britain, most of Europe and parts of Asia.

BLACK REDSTART

The black redstart (*Phoenicurus ochruros*) is named after red and black plumage. In the UK it is listed as an endangered bird; it feeds on insects, spiders, worms, berries and seeds.

FEEDING

For many birds the struggle to find sufficient food to survive is a near constant battle. While the spring and summer can be times of bounteous harvests, winter can be a time of tremendous hardship. As a general rule of thumb, the smaller the bird, the more critical the situation can become. This is because a small bird has far less in the way of fat reserves and so it cannot survive lean times as well as bigger birds. As humans we can make a lot of difference to their survival chances in the depths of winter by providing them with food—be it in the form of nuts, seeds or other suitable choices. Species such as the woodpecker will sometimes visit a bird table, but they are generally still able to find insects in rotten wood whatever time of year it is.

The lesser spotted woodpecker (*Dendrocopos minor*) is a sparrow-sized insect hunter of mature deciduous and mixed woods and orchards.

TREE CREEPER

The tree creeper (*Certhia familiaris*) is aptly named—it spends most of its time climbing up tree trunks holding on with specially adapted toes, looking for insects.

GREATER SPOTTED WOODPECKER

The greater spotted woodpecker (*Dendrocopos major*) builds its nest in holes in tree trunks. Although it primarily hunts for grubs in rotten wood, it will also kill and eat young nestlings.

Blue Tit

Many songbirds struggle to survive the winter, and human assistance—here in the form of a hanging feeder, can make all the difference to species such as these blue tits (*Parus caeruleus*).

FEEDING

HAMERKOP

The hamerkop (*Scopus umbretta*) likes to catch its prey while wading through shallow water. This individual has just caught an African bullfrog with its hook tipped beak.

RUFOUS HUMMINGBIRD

The rufous hummingbird (*Selasphorus rufus*), like the other members of this fascinating group of birds, hovers in front of flowers and uses its beak to access the energy-rich nectar.

COLLARED INCA HUMMIGBIRD

The collared Inca hummingbird (*Coeligena torquata*) is a spectacularly colored species with metallic green feathers. It comes from the cloud forests of Ecuador.

GREENFINCH

The greenfinch (*Carduelis chloris*) is a seed eater which gathers in flocks during the winter. It often visits bird tables in residential gardens.

Penguins – Order *Sphenisciformes*

Penguins

Penguins are quite unlike any other kind of bird—they cannot fly and yet they are often very successful with some species having colonies numbering in the thousands. The fact that they are able to thrive in the harshest of conditions is quite incredible, but the fact that some species are also able to foster their young in the depths of the Antarctic winters is absolutely amazing. The emperor penguin is a good example of this—they are the only birds on the planet which never set foot on dry land.

Other penguins live in places where they have to deal with harsh realities of a different kind. Killer whales and leopard seals will often lie in wait to prey on penguins as they leave their colonies. Once the unfortunate birds enter the water, these fierce predators attempt to pounce on them. As a way of maximising their chances, penguins will often dive in en masse, hoping to get through in the confusion. Sometimes they make it, and sometimes they don't!

Emperor penguins (*Aptenodytes forsteri*) are the only birds that never set foot on dry land. The male birds incubate the eggs by keeping them on their feet during the harsh Antarctic winter.

EMPEROR PENGUIN

Once the emperor penguin's egg has hatched, the chick also stays on its mother's feet to keep off the potentially lethal temperature of the snow—this youngster is being raised on the Brunt Ice Shelf, Antarctica.

ADELIE PENGUIN

The Adelie penguin (*Pygoscelis adeliae*) lives on ice-free, rocky coasts for much of the time. After breeding, however, they head out to the comparative safety of ice floes to molt.

443

ROCKHOPPER PENGUIN

Rockhopper penguins (*Eudyptes crestatus*) breed on most of the sub-Antarctic islands—the Falkland Islands have substantial colonies where the individuals seen here live.

ADELIE PENGUIN

The Adelie penguin feeds mostly on krill, which are small marine crustaceans   it will, however, also eat small fish and cephalopods if it gets the chance.

The Adelie penguin assembles in large colonies to breed. They are hunted by leopard seals and killer whales, so they enter the water by diving as a group to confuse such predators.

Other reptiles—including crocodiles, many turtles and snakes and a few lizards—have developed lifestyles that mean they spend most of their time in water. These species all still breathe air through their lungs and lay their eggs on land.

Reptiles can vary in size tremendously, although the adults of some species are less than an inch long—for example, the Jaragua lizard, (Sphaerodactylus ariasae)—the larger crocodiles can reach over 10ft (3m) in length, and weigh more than a ton.

The reptiles are divided into four separate orders: these are the order Crocodylia, which includes the crocodiles and alligators; the order Testudines, which includes the turtles and tortoises; the order Squamata which includes the lizards and snakes; and the order Rhynchocephalia which has only one living species— the lizard-like tuatara.

Turtles as a group have changed little for millions of years—they evolved to fill their ecological niches, and until mankind came along, they were doing very well at it. The largest sea-dwelling species is the leatherback turtle (Dermochelys coriacea), which can reach 1,500lb (680kg) in weight: it feeds primarily on jellyfish. The largest land-dwelling tortoise is the Galapagos giant tortoise (Geochelone elephantophus),

Loggerhead turtle eggs being removed to the safety of a wildlife sanctuary. Queensland

which is also very long-lived, with known individuals reaching well beyond the 100-year mark.

Turtles and tortoises are unique in that they have skeletons which have become modified to form external shells. This provides them with an excellent defence, especially once they have reached adulthood. Tortoises are able to withdraw their heads into their shells when attacked. Turtles, on the other hand, need to be streamlined in order to move through water quickly, and this means that they do not have room to do so. Having flippers instead of feet is another adaptation turtles have for life in the sea—this means that when they come onto land to lay their eggs they find it extremely hard to move.

Lizards are a group of reptiles that number thousands of different species—they have scales and claws, although in some species their legs are vestigial—that is, they are not visible externally. Examples of these are the glass lizards, slow worms and snake lizards. They also possess the ability to shed their tails when attacked—this is a process called autotomy. Lizards are able to re-grow their tail if they shed it, however, the new one is never as perfect as the original.

Although many lizards will bite if provoked, there are only two species which are venomous—these

A green turtle farm on the Cayman Islands.

The nocturnal fire salamander
(*Salamander salamander*) displays the fact
that it has toxic skin with vivid black and
yellow markings.

SALAMANDER

Neotony adult tadpole.

FROGS – ORDER ANURA

FROGS

Many people spent time as children watching tadpoles grow into baby frogs—as a result these wonderful creatures are well known to most of us. There are, however, many different kinds, and these range in size from the tiny poison arrow frogs of Central and South America to the massive horned frogs which can reach over a pound (half a kilo) in weight. Anyone who has spent time in the tropics will be well aware of the amount of noise that frogs can make. Many of these are tiny tree frogs, which can generate a lot more sound than most people would believe is possible! They tend to be very secretive, however, and it is almost impossible to approach most species of tree frogs in the wild without them ceasing their calls.

The common frog (*Rana temporaria*) is a terrestrial species which is found in Great Britain, Europe, and northwestern Asia.

TREE FROG

There are many different species of tree frogs—this is the Peruvian tree frog (*Osteocephalus taurinus*). It searches the branches and foliage of trees for the small creatures it feeds on.

Blue Poison Dart Frog

The blue poison dart or poison arrow frog (*Dendrobates azureus*) has bright warning colors to signal to predators that it has an extremely poisonous skin secretion.

YELLOW/BLUE POISON ARROW FROG
Native rainforest Amerindians use the toxins produced by various poison arrow frog species to make special coatings for their arrow tips—this helps them hunt and kill large animals.

RED-EYED TREE FROG

The red-eyed tree frog (*Agalychnis callidryas*) has, as its name would suggest, large prominent red eyes. It also has suckers on its toes which help it cling onto the undersides of leaves.

White's tree frog (*Litoria caerulea*) is a strange looking bright green jungle dwelling amphibian—it is also known as the dumpy tree frog and the smiling tree frog.

Frogs generally lay eggs in the form of spawn in ponds, lakes and other still or slow-moving bodies of fresh water. This is a common frog (*Rana temporaria*).

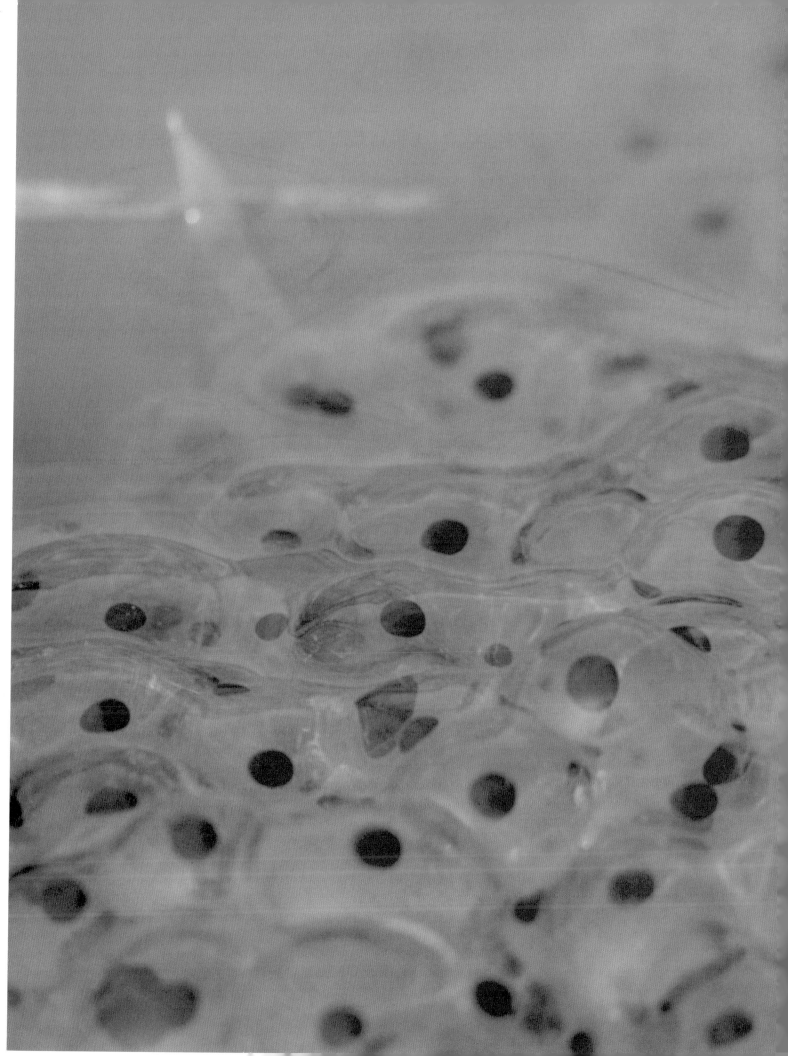

The cane toad (*Bufo marinus*) was introduced to Australia to control beetles which had become a major agricultural pest. Sadly, it then became a pest itself, wiping out many local amphibians.

DEAD LEAF TOAD

The dead leaf toad (*Bufo typhonius*) has amazingly effective camouflage—it hides on the floor of the Amazon rainforest where it can avoid predators and catch the small creatures it eats.

TURTLES

Turtles are distributed across the world. While most of the large ones are sea-going species, there are many different kinds of fresh water species too. Unfortunately, most of the sea turtles are threatened by mankind's activities. Some go to all the trouble of travelling thousands of miles across oceans to reach a particular beach to lay their eggs, only to have them stolen in minutes by humans. Others end up entangled in fishing nets where, since they are air-breathing animals, they are doomed to die by drowning. Luckily, there are lots of people who care about the welfare of turtles. There are conservation groups scattered all around the world which are doing their best to ensure that these marvellous creatures do not disappear altogether.

The hawksbill turtle (*Eretmochelys imbricata*) can be found swimming elegantly in most of the warm waters of the world.

GREEN TURTLE

These green turtle hatchlings (*Chelonia mydas*) are being reared in captivity to help build up their numbers for release into the wild.

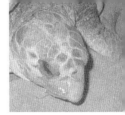

SEA TURTLE

When they break free of their eggshells, turtle hatchlings are extremely vulnerable to attack from predators—large seabirds take countless thousands of them before they make it to the sea.

SEA TURTLE

These two baby turtles have made it as far as the ocean's edge, but they will now have to face marine predators such as sharks which will be waiting their arrival.

LOGGERHEAD TURTLE

Loggerhead turtles (*Caretta caretta*) are an endangered species—here a female is laying eggs on a sandy beach in Queensland, Australia.

Female loggerhead turtles are not well suited to moving on land, but in order to lay their eggs, they must crawl up a sandy beach and dig a deep hole.

The Galapagos giant tortoise is very popular with tourists. It is a very slow-moving animal, and can only reach 0.16mph (0.26kph).

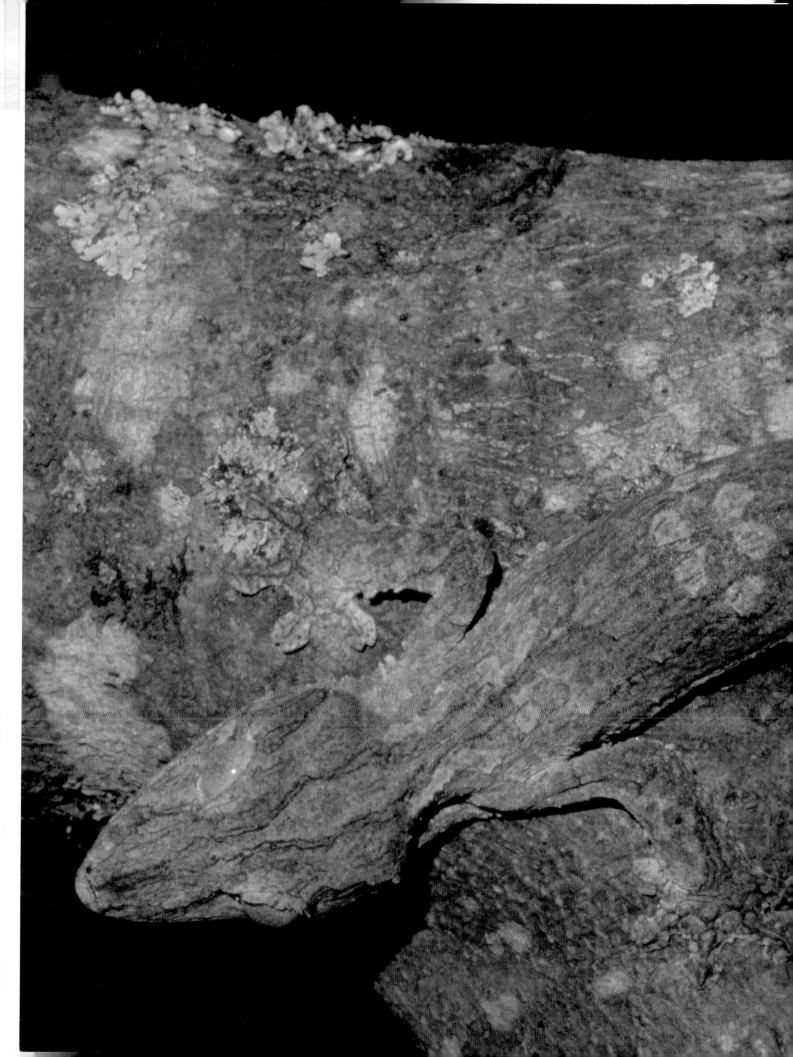

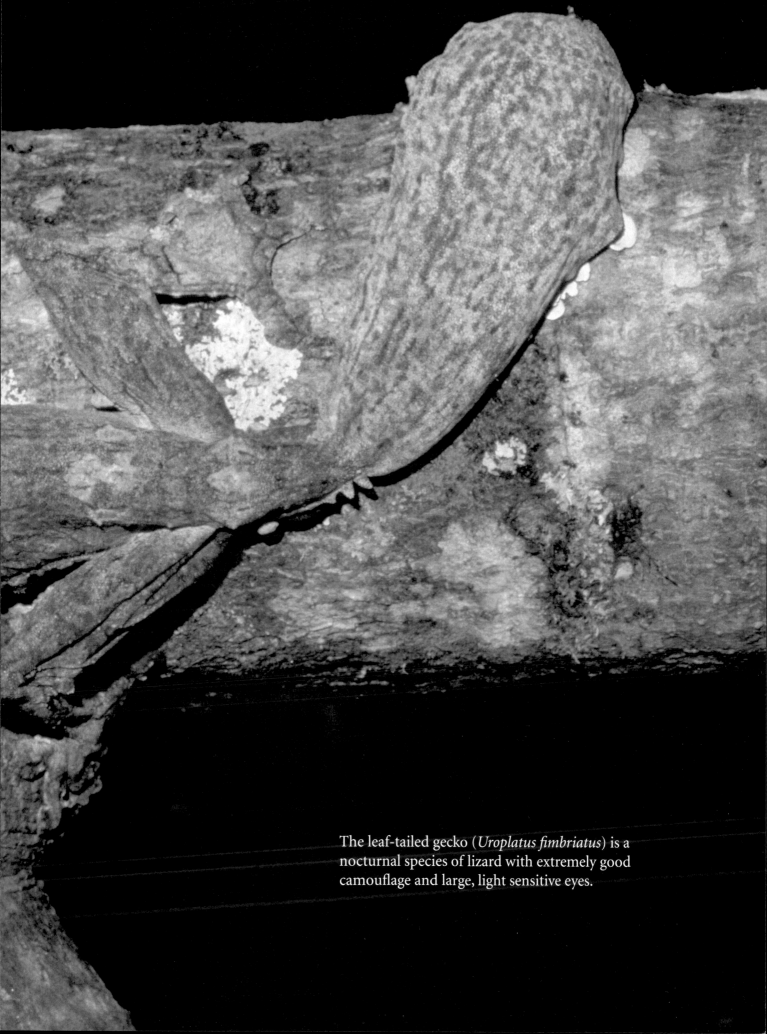

The leaf-tailed gecko (*Uroplatus fimbriatus*) is a
nocturnal species of lizard with extremely good
camouflage and large, light sensitive eyes.

KOMODO DRAGON

The komodo dragon (*Varanus komodensis*) is the largest lizard in the world, growing to 10ft (3m) long. They are powerful carnivores, and feed on deer and other animals.

MARINE IGUANA

The marine iguana (*Amblyrhynchus cristatus*) is exclusive to the Galapagos Islands, far out in the Pacific Ocean. Uniquely, they feed on seaweed—the larger individuals even dive to do so.

AGAMA LIZARD

The common agama lizard (*Agama agama*) is a social species, which is often found in groups in its native East Africa.

ANOLIS LIZARD

There are about 300 different species in the group of anolis lizards. This image shows is a Graham's anolis lizard (*Anolis grahami*) licking nectar from a jungle flower.

A close up of the head of a Tokay gecko (*Gekko gecko*) shows the unusual colors and rough skin on its head. They live in tropical rainforests, where they seek out cliffs and trees.

THORNY DEVIL

The Australian thorny devil (*Moloch horridus*) is a fearsome looking beast—it is, however, completely harmless. It is adapted to cope with high daytime desert temperatures.

ORNATE DAY GECKO

The ornate day gecko (*Phelsuma ornata*) is, as its name would suggest a highly colored diurnal lizard. It is also one of the smallest reptiles in the world ranging in length from 0.6in (1.5cm) to 1in (2.5cm).

SNAKES

Snakes are probably only rivalled by spiders when it comes to human phobias. For some reason some people cannot enter a room if there is a snake present; others, however, can't get enough of them, and like to keep them as pets. The Californian king snake is particularly popular for this as it is reasonably easy to keep in captivity. While there are arguments for and against keeping any animal caged up, the boa constrictor has been encouraged to take up residence in jungle huts by native tribes people to kill rats since the dawn of creation. Some species are far too dangerous for all but the most experienced to handle. These include the vipers and mambas, which are deadly and should never be approached. The cobra, however, is an extremely venomous snake which has been used by snake charmers for entertainment purposes for thousands of years.

The parrot snake (*Leptophis ahaetulla*) is distributed throughout the forested areas of South America between Mexico and Argentina.

AMAZONIAN TREE-VIPER

The Amazonian tree-viper (*Bothrops bilineatus*) hunts rodents and other small animals in the rainforests of the Amazon delta and surrounding areas.

The green mamba (*Dendroaspis viridis*) is a highly venomous
and fast moving snake. This one has just caught a rodent
which it is in the process of swallowing.

CALIFORNIAN KING SNAKE

The Californian king snake (*Getulus californiae*) has very variable markings. The adults grow to about 3ft (90cm) long, and favor dry areas where they feed on small animals including rattlesnakes.

SWAMP SNAKE

This velvety swampsnake (*Liophis typhlus*) which can be found in the Amazon rainforest has just caught a leaf frog (*Phyllomedusa tomopterna*) and is in the process of swallowing it.

Boa Constrictor

The boa constrictor (*Constrictor constrictor*) is a non-venomous snake which feeds on small rodents. It is found in Central and South America and often reaches lengths of up to 13ft (4m).

BOA CONSTRICTOR

Boa constrictors are such efficient hunters that native tribes people often keep them in their homes to keep the rat population down.

The gaboon viper (*Bitis gabonica*) has a lethal bite—its venom can kill an adult human in less than 15 minutes. It lives in the equatorial belt of Tropical Africa.

ADDER

The adder or viper (*Vipera berus*) is the only venomous reptile to be found in the British Isles. It is a small snake with a distinctive continuous zigzag down its back.

INDIAN COBRA

The Indian cobra (*Naja naja*) is a highly venomous snake which grows to about 5ft (1.5m) long. It occurs throughout India, Pakistan, and Sri Lanka.

CROCODILES

Crocodiles and alligators are large reptiles that are supremely adapted for life as swimming predators. They are so well fitted to this role that they have changed little in millions of years. Their eyes, ears and nostrils are located along the top of the head so that they can remain almost entirely underwater, and thus unseen by their prey until it is too late. They even have a third eyelid and muscles to close the nostrils—these help protect them while they are underwater. They have mouths which are packed with sharp teeth, and very powerful jaw muscles which allow them to bite through the toughest hide. There are many different species in this group, including fish-eating ones from India and dwarf ones from South America.

The American alligator (*Alligator mississippiensis*) is the largest reptile in North America, reaching over 16ft (5m) from head to tail.

CROCODILE

A large adult Nile crocodile (*Crocodylus niloticus*) such as this individual lying in the sun is a ferocious predator which will kill anything it can catch, including lions and humans.

The Jacare caiman (*Caiman yacare*) which lives in the wetlands, rivers and lakes of many parts of South America has been hunted for years—its skin is used to make boots, handbags, and belts.

Insects can be found almost wherever you go on this earth—they inhabit everything from the coldest mountains to the hottest deserts. They are, however, predominantly creatures of land and fresh water. While there are some insect species that live in the sea, they are few in number in comparison to the amount of salt water on the planet. Some insects permanently live in the dark, either under the soil or in caves, whereas others fly in the glare of the sun.

With the exception of submarine ocean habitats, if there is a food source to be had, insects will be exploiting it. Although there are huge numbers of insects that only ever eat vegetable matter, masses of others are voracious carnivores. There are parasites, scavengers, blood suckers, aerial gladiators and terrestrial refuse collectors. The world of insects is, indeed, a fascinating place.

Insects have been on the planet for at least 350 million years: for the first 150 million, they were the only creatures with the power of flight. During this era some insects grew incredibly large—huge dragonflies dominated the skies for a very long time. It is highly likely that the first vertebrate animals developed the ability to fly simply to catch and eat insects.

The fact the insects have been around for so long

Many butterfly species such as these swallowtails (*Papilio machaon*) like to gather around puddles and on damp soil to soak up vital mineral salts.

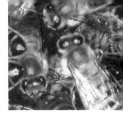

has resulted in there being an enormous variety of them. No one knows how many different species there are alive today. Although around one million have been identified, estimates of how many there are in total vary between ten and a hundred million. In the polar wastes the number of species able to survive is very small; however, the tropical rainforests teem with all manner of weird and wonderful creatures.

An adult insect is technically made up of a head with a pair of antennae; a thorax with three pairs of legs and (usually) two pairs of wings; and an abdomen with the digestive and reproductive organs.

All this is encased in a hard-jointed exoskeleton. Insects breathe air, but have no means of pumping it through the body. Instead there is a system of spiracles—these are small passages which allow air to reach deep into the body tissues. Those species of insects which live underwater have to come to the surface to breathe.

Insects have four distinct stages to their lifecycles. They start off as an egg, which then hatches into a larva (also called a caterpillar, nymph, grub or worm); this then pupates—a dormant stage where the larva undergoes great changes. The pupa (also called a chrysalis) may be encased in a cocoon that splits

A swarm of bees may number several thousand individuals.

open and the adult insect emerges. If all goes well, the cycle will then start all over again.

Insects vary in size tremendously, but they cannot grow bigger than a certain size because their breathing systems cannot function if their bodies get more than about an inch and a half wide. The biggest insects—such as the Atlas moth (Attacus atlas) may measure as much as a foot (0.3m) across, but most of this size is made up of wings. There are species of stick insects, such as Pharnacia kirbyi, where the females can be over 1ft 2in (36cm) long, but their bodies are still less than 1.5in (3.8cm) wide. The Acteon beetle (Megasoma acteon) from South America grows to the maximum possible size for an insect—males of this species can reach 3.5in (9cm) long and be an 1.5in (3.8cm) deep. There are several other giants in the insect world—these include the rare South American longhorn beetle (Titanus giganteus) and the Hercules beetle (Dynastes hercules), both of which reach over 6.5in (16cm)

long.

The vast majority of insects, however, are very small indeed. These include many thousands of species of beetles which are less than four hundredths of an inch (1mm) long. There are many species of wasps and ants which are tiny when fully grown. The insect which is currently thought to be the smallest in the world is a parasitic wasp which has no common name—its scientific name is Megaphragma caribea. It comes from Guadeloupe and only reaches about eight thousandths of an inch (0.17mm) long.

Other insect species may not be particularly large as individuals but they can more than make up for this with numbers. The order Orthoptera, which contains the many species of grasshopper and locust, is a good example. Swarms of the African desert locust (Schistocerca gregaria), for instance, can contain as many as 28,000,000,000 individuals, which if combined would weigh in the order of

Many ant species become fearsome predators when they assemble in large numbers. The individuals seen here have captured an assassin bug.

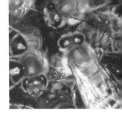

70,000 tons.

The order Hymenoptera can also produce staggering numbers—the ants are social insects which often live in massive colonies. It is reported, for example, that a single supercolony made up of 45,000 interconnected nests of the Japanese ant *Formica yessensis* contained 1,080,000 queens and 306,000,000 workers.

There are about 32 separate orders of insects—the exact definitions of which are still being established by scientists. The largest family covers the Colcoptera, or beetles, with about half a million different species. The insects that are the best known and loved are the Lepidoptera—the butterflies and moths. Other insect orders include the Odonata: these are the magnificent dragonflies and damselflies.

The order Diptera, which are the true flies, can be distinguished from other flying insects because they only have a single pair of functional wings. Being insects, however, they do have a second pair, but it is so reduced that it is not apparent to anything but the closest scrutiny. The order Ephemeroptera includes the mayflies—these are small flying insects which begin life as aquatic nymphs. When they emerge from their pupal cases they experience a brief adulthood—usually lasting only a day or so—before dying. The stoneflies are in the order Plecoptera: these also begin their lives in water and emerge as flying adults; however, they survive as adults for a week or more. The phasmids and stick insects are in the order Phasmidae—these are strange-looking tropical and subtropical creatures that mimic twigs and leaves. The true bugs are members of the order Hemiptera—these are insects with sucking mouthparts. Although most feed on plant sap, many are carnivorous and prey on other insects. The order Aphidae are exclusively plant sap feeders and include the greenfly, blackfly and aphids. There are many other orders of insects, including those which contain the fleas and termites.

Termites (*Isoptera sp.*) can be found throughout the tropical and subtropical areas of the world where they often cause huge amounts of damage to timber structures.

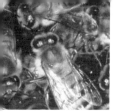

BUTTERFLIES & MOTHS

Butterflies are well known and liked by most people, even those who live in cities. They are usually considered to be colourful, and for the most part, harmless, creatures. Moths, on the other hand, are generally thought of as small brown things that fly at night and eat clothes, or words to that effect. It is a surprise to many, therefore, that lots of moths are as brightly coloured as butterflies, that many fly during the day and none, as adults, actually eat clothes.

One of the most common questions when this subject is approached, is 'what is the difference between a butterfly and a moth?' Technically, there is no easy answer to this—whatever rule one imposes is broken by one or more species somewhere. For instance, the concept that moths fold their wings flat and butterflies hold them upright is as wrong as wrong can be. The Geometridae, for example, is a massive family of moths that comprises many thousands of species—most of which can hold their wings upright. Some people say that butterflies have clubbed antennae, but moths do not—this is also fallacious. It is probably best not to worry too much about such detail—far better to enjoy the spectacle of them all!

Butterflies and moths are most numerous in the tropical areas of the world, especially the rainforests where they can teem in countless millions. In the temperate regions there are still lots to be seen, but in the colder places they can be few in number, or absent altogether. in the colder places they can be few in number, or absent altogether.

The silver-studded blue (*Plebejus argus*) is an uncommon European butterfly which occurs in small colonies on heathland.

MONARCH

This is the caterpillar of the monarch butterfly (*Danaus plexippus*) which is also known as the "wanderer" due to the adult's ability to cover thousands of miles with ease.

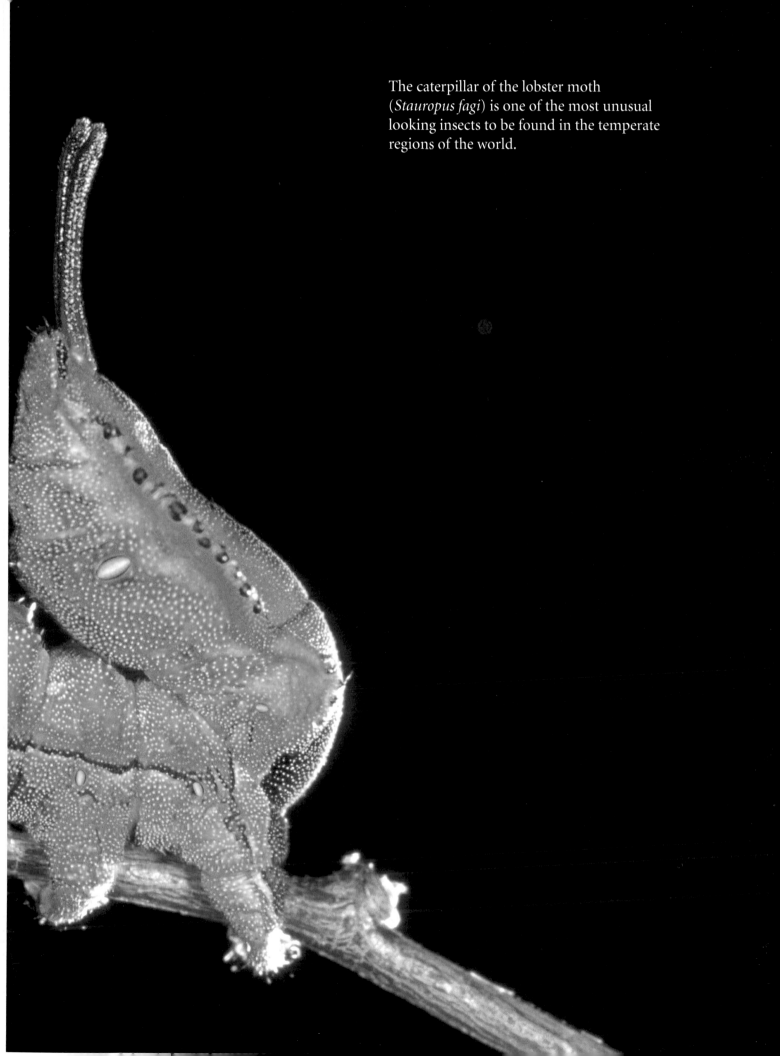

The caterpillar of the lobster moth (*Stauropus fagi*) is one of the most unusual looking insects to be found in the temperate regions of the world.

The brown peacock butterfly (*Anartia amathea*) is distributed throughout South America and the West Indies. It is common throughout its range and frequently visits flowers.

The geometrid moth, *Agathia antitheta*, which comes from Papua New Guinea settles with its wings flat so that its mottled green markings provide good camouflage.

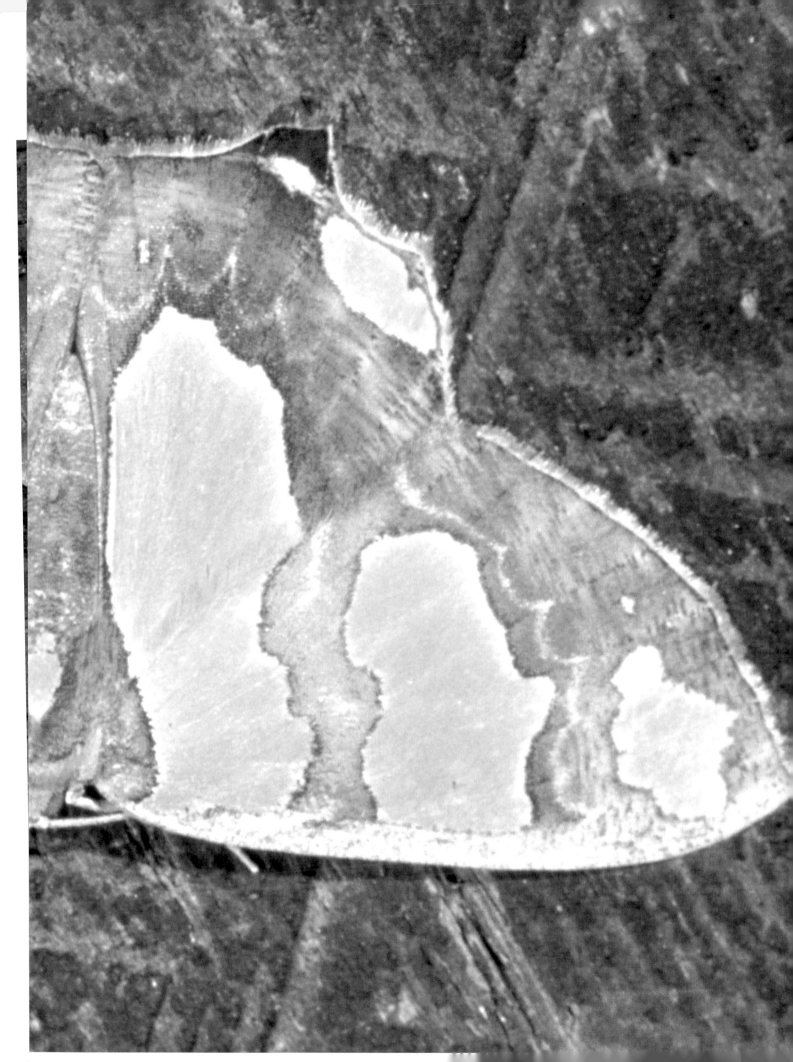

RAINFOREST MOTH

This rainforest moth (*Lasiocampidae sp.*) has developed an effective defence mechanism—it has evolved to look just like a fearsome wolf spider.

SPURGE HAWK CATERPILLAR

The caterpillar of the spurge hawk moth (*Hyles euphorbia*) is aposematic—that is, it displays warning colors to show it is poisonous.

There are thousands of different species of inch measuring worms around the world. They are all members of the *Geometridae* family. This example comes from the Amazon rainforest.

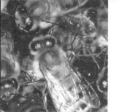

BEETLES

Beetles are the most numerous order of animals on the planet, with at least half a million species known to man. The vast majority of these have no commercial impact on human activity as they live deep in the tropical rainforests of the world; however, a small number of species do have great significance, especially to the agricultural industry. Anywhere there is a crop being grown, or there is bulk storage of food, there will be beetles trying to eat their way through it. This includes potatoes, grain, maize, flour and all manner of other foodstuffs. Sometimes the adult beetles will be the problem, but generally it is the larvae or grubs that do the most damage.

On a more positive note, there are beetles which play a beneficial role—for instance, the ladybirds (Coccinella sp.), are voracious hunters of aphids both as larvae and adults. A small number of them can massacre entire colonies of greenfly, blackfly or other similar species in a very short time. Many other beetles, such as the Tiger beetles (Cicindella sp.) are also very helpful as they can be very efficient predators of garden pests. The dung beetles also do a tremendous service—not only do they consume massive quantities of animal waste, but they also drag a lot of it underground, and in doing so help to fertilise the soil. The Scarab beetle, with its golden wing cases, was revered by the Ancient Egyptians, and to this day it is still collected to make jewellery.

The distinctive giraffe beetle (*Coloeptera sp.*) has a remarkably long neck—it is a rare species which can only be found in Madagascar.

GEM BEETLE

The gem beetle (*Pachyrhynchus gemmatus*) lives deep in the rainforest in Papua New Guinea where its sparkling colors are used for mate attraction.

The elephant horned scarab beetle (*Diloboderus abderus*) from Uruguay has a heavily armored exoskeleton for protection.

LADYBIRD

The 7-spot ladybird (*Coccinella 7-punctata*) is an insect that is beneficial to mankind due to its rapacious appetite for aphids.

LANTERN BUG

The lantern bug (*Laternaria laternaria*) from Peru is normally well concealed, but can flash its eye spots to scare off potential predators if discovered.

OTHERS

There are many insects that have significance to mankind—from bees which provide us with honey to termites which destroy houses and other timber structures in many of the tropical and subtropical areas of the world. There are insects that help us by killing all manner of pests—things like preying mantids and dragonflies take enormous numbers of mosquitoes, flies and other harmful species. Other insects live far from mankind in remote jungles where they have no direct impact on human activity—this doesn't mean that we should ignore them, however, and those that are endangered need all the help they can get.

This preying mantis nymph (*Chlidonoptera chopardi*) from West Africa has a long way to grow before it reaches the size of its parents.

TREE HOPPER

The rainforests of the world are full of strange and wonderful looking creatures—this Philippine tree hopper (*Emphius bakeri*) is equipped with decorative armored horns.

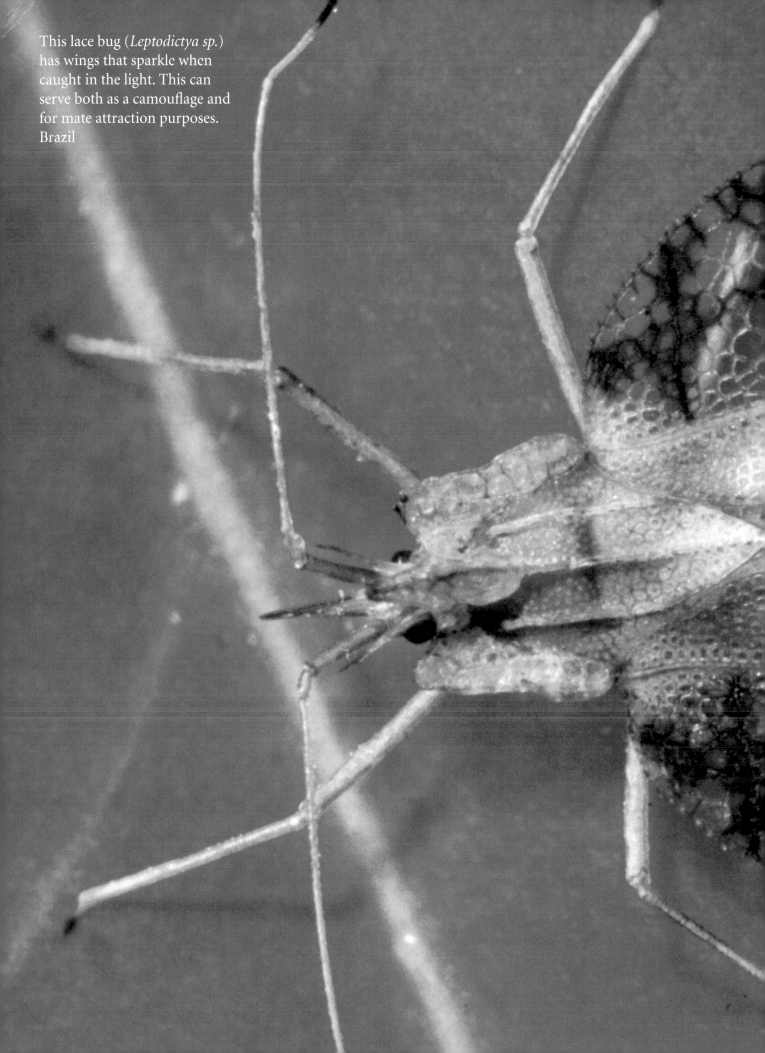

This lace bug (*Leptodictya sp.*) has wings that sparkle when caught in the light. This can serve both as a camouflage and for mate attraction purposes. Brazil

There are many different kinds of animals that come under the banner of invertebrates. The biggest group is the class of arthropods—this contains the insects, which we have already considered, however, there are many more. Arthropods are animals that have a jointed external skeleton made out of a protein called chitin. Whereas insects only have six legs, other arthropods may have many more: spiders have eight legs; lobsters which usually also have eight can, in fact, have more; and millipedes can have up to 200.

The biggest arthropods are the lobsters and crabs—some of these, such as the giant spider crab (Macrocheira kaempferi) can have claw spans of 9ft (2.75m) or more. The smallest are the pea crabs in the family Pinnotheridae, which are only about 0.25in (6.25mm) across the shell. An Atlantic lobster (Homarus americanus) which was caught in 1934 holds the record for being the heaviest crustacean—it weighed in at more than 42lb (19kg)! The smallest arthropods are the mites, which are members of the same grouping as the spiders.

There are at least 40,000 species of crustaceans in the world, including the crayfish, lobsters, barnacles, woodlice, crabs and shrimps. Most of these are aquatic, and occur in both fresh and salt water. The arachnids are even more numerous than the crustaceans, with some 75,000 species being known to man. They include the scorpions, mites, ticks and spiders. There are also something like 13,000 species of myriapods—these are the many-legged creatures such as the centipedes and millipedes.

Spiders are in the family Araneae—their bodies are divided into two major parts—the prosoma, which is

The fan worm (*Spirographis spallanzani*) lives below the sea bed in a papery tube. It throws out a highly ornate fan-like structure which it uses to filter out food from the water around it.

a combination of the head and the thorax, and the opisthosoma which equates to the abdomen. The last two abdominal segments in spiders are specially modified into spinnerets—these secrete the silk threads which many species use to build their webs. Not all spiders are web-builders, however, since many stalk or ambush their prey. These include the wolf spiders, tarantulas, and jumping spiders. Nearly all spiders use poison to overcome their prey—in some species this can be toxic enough to cause severe injury or even death to humans. Examples of these are the redback spider from Australia and the black widow from North America. Some spiders are large enough to capture and kill small birds; for example, the Goliath bird-eating spider (Theraphosa leblondi) which comes from South America has a legs which can measure as much as 11in (28cm)

across.

Scorpions also belong to the arachnid grouping. These are characterised by having a pair of claws at the head end, and a tail tipped by a sting—this is equipped with a pair of poison glands. The toxins used vary from species to species, and while they are all used to paralyse prey, some are more dangerous than others. Some of those found in northern Africa and the American southwest can be fatal to humans. All scorpions are carnivorous and most prey on insects, although some are capable of killing and eating small rodents as well. They tend to be nocturnal, and spend the day hiding in mouse holes, under rocks, or in crevices.

Molluscs are also classed as invertebrates—they are a successful group with over 160,000 species being recorded. Of these, 128,000 are still alive today,

This beautifully colored orange and red Indonesian starfish (*Fromia monilia*), is a striking member of the echinoderm family.

with the other 35,000 being known from fossils. They occur on almost every habitat on land and in water. They can be found at the depths of the deepest oceans and at the tops of the highest trees, and one form of mollusc or another has evolved to fill almost every ecological niche between these extremes. The most numerous form of molluscs are those known as gastropods—this group includes the slugs, snails and many of the species generally referred to as seashells. The bivalves are the second largest group—this also includes many seashells, such as the oyster, mussel and many others.

Although the molluscs are usually thought of as a group which is comprised of snails and the like, many people are surprised to find that it also covers the cephalopods: the squid, octopus and cuttlefish. Instead of the large muscular foot which is found in most seashell species, these amazing creatures have arms or tentacles. They also tend to have very good sight, a facility that helps them both in hunting prey and in social communication. Many cephalopod species assemble in large numbers, and they often have very complex interactions between them. Some of these have special skin cells which can change colour. While this is used as camouflage to hide from predators or to stalk prey, it is also used as a signalling mechanism. Certain species are able to convey entirely different messages on each side of

This spectacular creature is called a crevice crinoid (*Comanthus parvicirrus*) it can be seen in many places throughout the Indian ocean.

the body—this way they can keep their conversations private if they want to.

All of the 13,000 species of myriapods are terrestrial. Although they often have names like millipede (which means one thousand feet) and centipede (which means one hundred feet), some species have less than ten pairs of legs. Others, however, can have nearly 200. The smallest species are barely visible to the naked eye, and the biggest are around 12in (30cm) long. Many myriapods have special glands which produce toxins—these are used to poison prey, and although they can give humans painful bites, they are not poisonous enough to be fatal.

The jellyfish, sea anemones and corals all belong to a large group called the phylum Cnidaria, (formerly called the coelenterates). The phylum Echinodermata contains a range of entirely marine animals including the crinoids (sea lilies and feather stars) as well as the starfish and brittle stars. Sponges, which belong to the 'Porifera' are also invertebrates, for although they may look like plants, they are actually animals. Different species live in fresh and salt water, where they feed by filtering small plants and animals out of water.

The giant centipede (*Scolopendra gigantea*) is a native of South American jungles where it can grow to over a foot (30cm) in length. It has a toxic bite.

SPIDERS

Spiders play an important part in the many different ecosystems of the world. They are very effective predators on all manner of small creatures, from the tiniest of aphids to mice, rats and other rodents. Some spiders use webs to catch their victims, whereas other species, like the jumping spider, stalk their prey and then pounce on it from a short range. Without spiders keeping a check on their numbers, we would soon be overrun by fast-breeding pests like flies and mosquitoes. The reduction in numbers of such harmful creatures by spiders means that we don't have to use nearly as many pesticides as we would otherwise, which is clearly good for the planet.

The jumping spider (*Phidippus sp.*) has four simple eyes in front, and two on each side. This example is feeding on a fruit fly.

GARDEN SPIDER

The garden spider (*Araneus diadematus*) lives mostly in grassland areas where it uses an orb web to trap its prey. It then wraps its catch in silk before consuming it.

MOLLUSCS – SEASHELLS

Seashells have been of interest to mankind since the earliest times. Mussels, oysters, clams and many other species have been an important food source to many civilisations for many thousands of years. They have been used as utensils, musical instruments, art objects and as agricultural fertilisers. Some of the less common seashells were used as currency by many human societies for hundreds, if not thousands, of years. Some of the more desirable species were used to barter for slaves, and large numbers of unfortunate souls were traded for them over the years. During the 1700s and well into the late 1800s it became very fashionable for well to do people to collect seashells. While it may be that pressure was put on certain species by collectors, without this interest we would certainly have a lot less information about them—after all, we are only able to conserve creatures that we know about.

The massive tridacna clam is another species which is under threat from over-fishing—their meat is considered a delicacy.

QUEEN CONCH

The queen conch (*Strombus gigas*) is a marine mollusc that is hunted extensively for its meat. Consequently thousands of these beautiful shells end up discarded on beaches.

MOLLUSCS – SQUID & OCTOPUS

The cephalopods are a fascinating group of marine animals—they include the squid, octopus and nautilus. The word cephalopod means head-foot, and refers to the fact that they have tentacles or arms emanating from close to their heads. It is known that they have very well-developed brains, and it is almost certain that they are the most intelligent members of the invertebrate world. Although they are closely related to the seashells, only the nautilus has retained its external shell. The cuttlefish has a large oval internal cuttlebone, while the squid has a structure called a pen, which looks like a piece of clear plastic. The octopus, which is considered to be the most advanced member of the group, has lost all remnants of a shell. The many cephalopod species are distributed all over the seas of the world, from the freezing waters of the poles to the midst of the tropics, proving that they are not just an interesting group, but also a successful one.

The many species of cuttlefish (*Sepia sp.*) all have remarkable eyesight which they use for hunting as well as for social interaction.

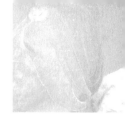

Molluscs – Squid & Octopus – Class *Cephalopoda*

Cuttlefish

The cuttlefish is a cephalopod which is a master of disguise—it can change the color of its skin to blend in with the background.

571

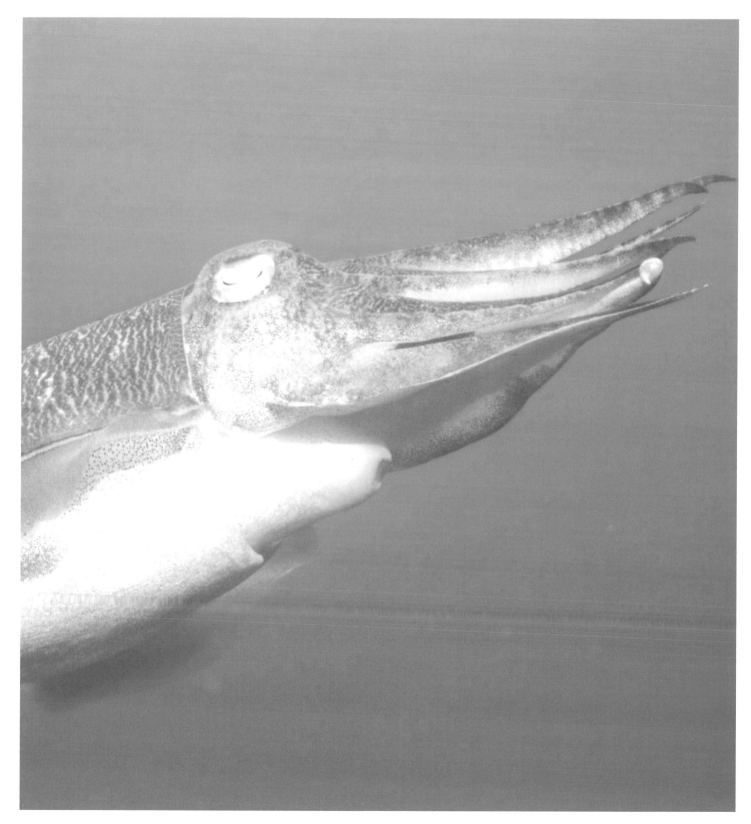

CUTTLEFISH

The cuttlefish is a voracious predator, hunting all manner of small fish, shrimps and other animals. This species is from the Gulf of Oman.

Cuttlefish

Not only can cuttlefish blend in squid their surroundings by changing their skin color, but they can also use the same means to communicate with others in their group.

OCTOPUS

The octopus is a good swimmer, and uses its eight powerful tentacles which are armed with suckers to capture its prey.

OCTOPUS

The common moctopus (*Octopus vulgaris*) occurs in tropical and subtropical waters—this example was photographed in the Mediterreanean Sea.

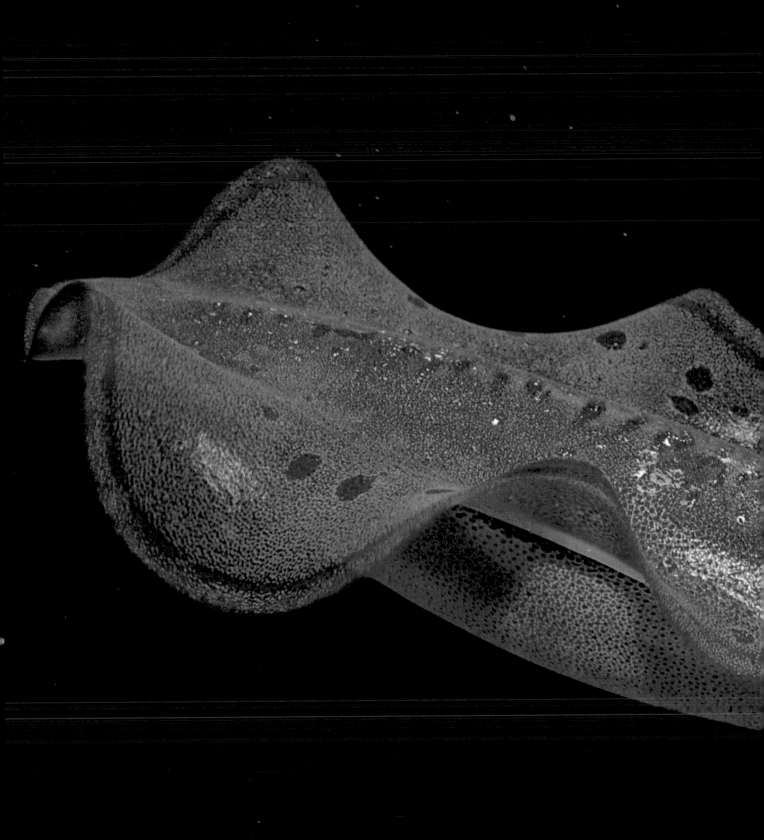

The bigfin reef squid (*Sepioteuthis lessoniana*) grows
to around 10in (25cm) in length and occurs in shallow
coastal waters throughout the Indo-Pacific region.

CRUSTACEANS

The order Crustacea includes species as small as the water fleas (Daphnia sp.) as well as the much larger lobsters and crabs. While there are some successful land species, such as woodlice, the majority of the group are aquatic. There are many different classes within the order of crustaceans. For instance, the ostracods are a class of very small bean-shaped creatures that swim in fresh and salt water where they filter minute particles of food as they move. The branchiopods are the group of fresh water organisms that includes the water fleas, whereas the copepods are mostly marine. They teem in their untold billions in the oceans of the world, and are a major source of food for all manner of larger animals, and form a large part of the diet of things like the baleen whales, basking sharks, and other filter feeders. The class Malacostraca includes about two-thirds of all the crustaceans, and covers all the larger species, such as the woodlice, shrimps, crabs and lobsters.

The common lobster (*Homarus gammarus*) is a commercially important species. It has powerful pincers which it uses for defence as well as to crush and cut up prey.

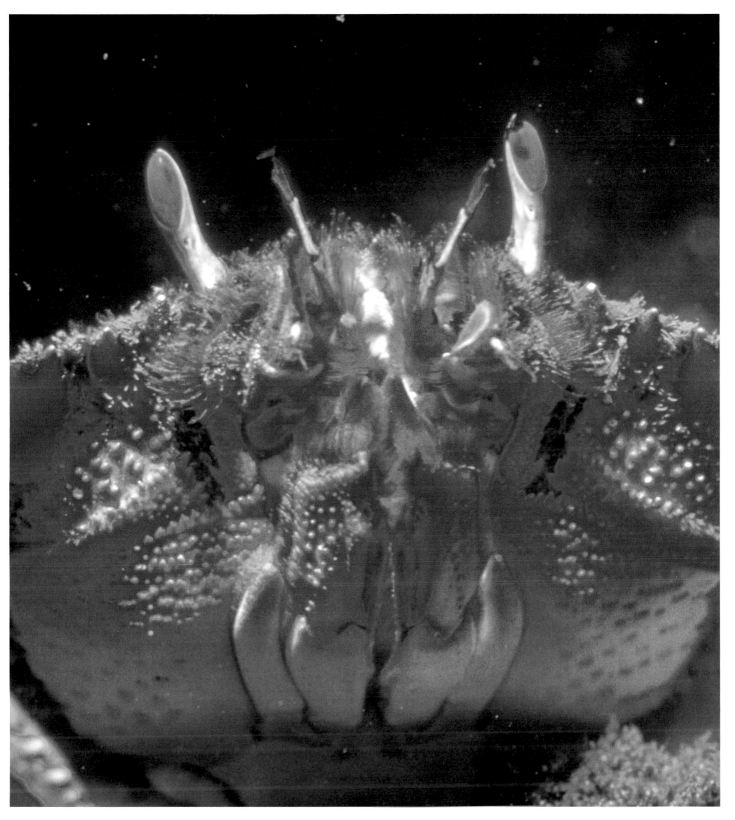

CRAB

Crabs are opportunists—they will eat anything from decaying matter to plant matter or any small animals vthey can catch.

BANDED BOXING SHRIMP

The magnificent banded boxing shrimp (*Stenopus hispidus*) can be found in shallow tropical waters across the world where it feeds on small fish or crustaceans.

REEF CRAB

Reef crab" is a general term for crabs that are not associated with some other distinctive characteristic or niche, and typically roam the reef without being confined to a certain piece of coral or host.

The spiny squat lobster (*Galathea strigosa*) can be found in European waters from the Mediterranean Sea up to the coasts of Norway.

JELLYFISH

Jellyfish are familiar to anyone who swims in the sea or walks on the beach on a regular basis. They can be as small as 0.5in (12.5mm) long to more than 6ft (2m) across. The jellyfish with the longest tentacles is called Cyanea arctica: in this species they can reach over 130ft (40m) long! Some are able to give the unwary swimmer a mild rash, whereas others can even cause death. While some jellyfish are eaten by animals like turtles and sea birds, they are not consumed by many humans—the biggest market for them is in Japan.

Jellyfish can be found in most of the oceans and seas of the world—this species feeds on plankton in deep oceanic waters.

Jellyfish - *Phylum Cnidaria*

Jellyfish

Jellyfish (*Scyphozoa*) come in all shapes and sizes—this species is a large free swimming marine organism which has thousands of stinging cells on its long tentacles.

Jellyfish have very limited control over where they drift,
however, they can change their depth to take advantage of the
whereabouts of the plankton on which they feed.

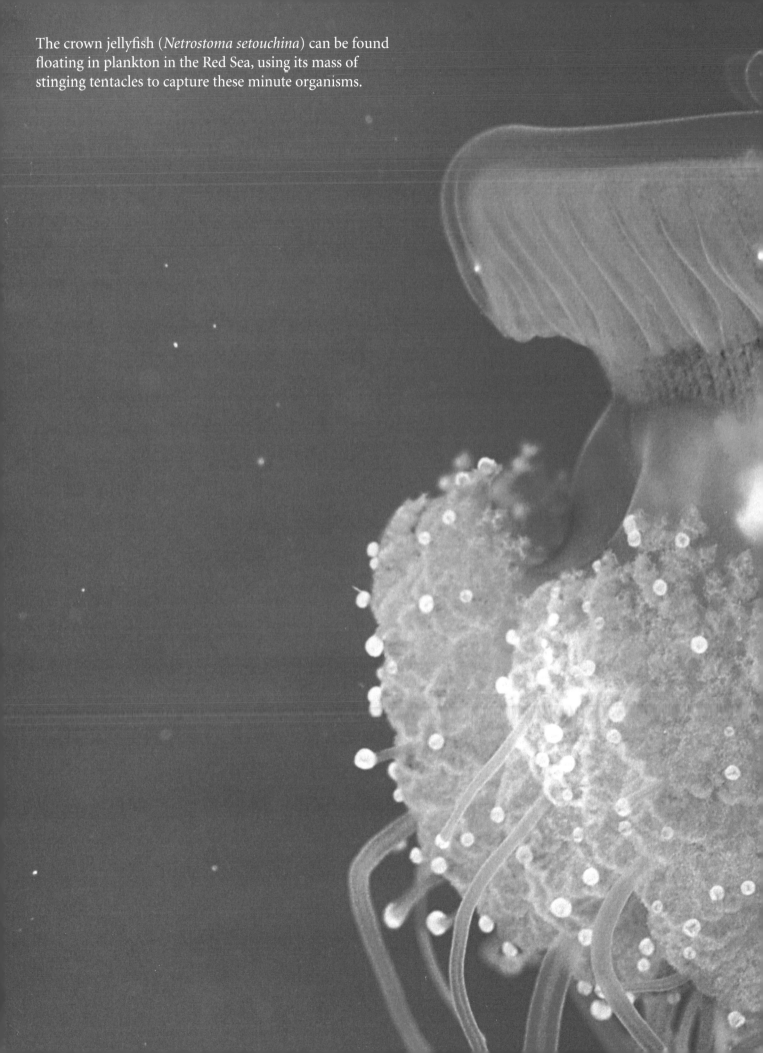

The crown jellyfish (*Netrostoma setouchina*) can be found floating in plankton in the Red Sea, using its mass of stinging tentacles to capture these minute organisms.

STARFISH & SEA URCHINS

Starfish and sea urchins are for the most part predators. Since they move quite slowly, they are unable to catch fast-moving prey like fish, so instead they feed on molluscs, barnacles or, in the case of species such as the crown of thorns, live coral. Starfish and sea urchins have no front or back, and so are able to move in any direction just as easily. Instead of using their five or more legs to move around, starfish have hundreds of tiny legs which end in a sucker. These are all linked together and powered by a complex hydraulic system. This is powerful enough for a starfish to be able to cling to rocks and withstand strong tidal currents that would otherwise dislodge them. If a starfish loses one of its legs, it is able to grow a new one to replace it. Amazingly, if a starfish is cut in half, each piece will grow into a new, complete starfish. Sea urchins also use a similar method to move around.

Starfish thrive on coral reefs—this example (*Bothriaster primigenius*), lives in the waters off the Philippines where it browses on algea and coral polyps.

Blue Linckia Starfish

The stunning blue linckia starfish seen here grow to about four inches across. They can be found on coral reefs where they move around eating algae and small creatures.

ORANGE STARFISH

This orange starfish occurs in the Caribbean, and like the other members of the family, it feeds on all manner of living and dead animal matter.

Starfish

Starfish wait for a particular combination of tidal and light conditions before spawning—this example is releasing eggs over a reef near the Galapagos Islands.

The crown-of-thorns starfish has a voracious appetite for live hard-corals—it also breeds incredibly fast, and as a result has been responsible for untold damage to coral reefs.

STARFISH

Starfish (*Asteroidea sp.*) are predators which often prey on different mollusc species—the example shown here is using its tube feet to pull a mussel shell apart before consuming it.

Fire Urchin

The fire urchin is covered by venomous spines—these provide a very effective defence which is capable of inflicting intensely painful wounds on would-be attackers.

NUDIBRANCHS

Nudibranchs—which are more commonly known as sea slugs—belong to a group of molluscs called the opisthobranchs. They are very similar to seashells, except that they have lost their shells, in much the same way as land slugs are basically snails without shells. The name nudibranch actually means naked gill, and refers to the feathery structures that function as external respiratory organs. Sea slugs are often very vividly coloured—this is to warn potential predators to stay away as they are poisonous. These beautiful creatures are sometimes found in rock pools where they often cause much excitement amongst onlookers.

Nudibranchs are often vividly colored to warn predators that they have a toxic content. They usually also have long, feathery projections on their backs through which they breathe.

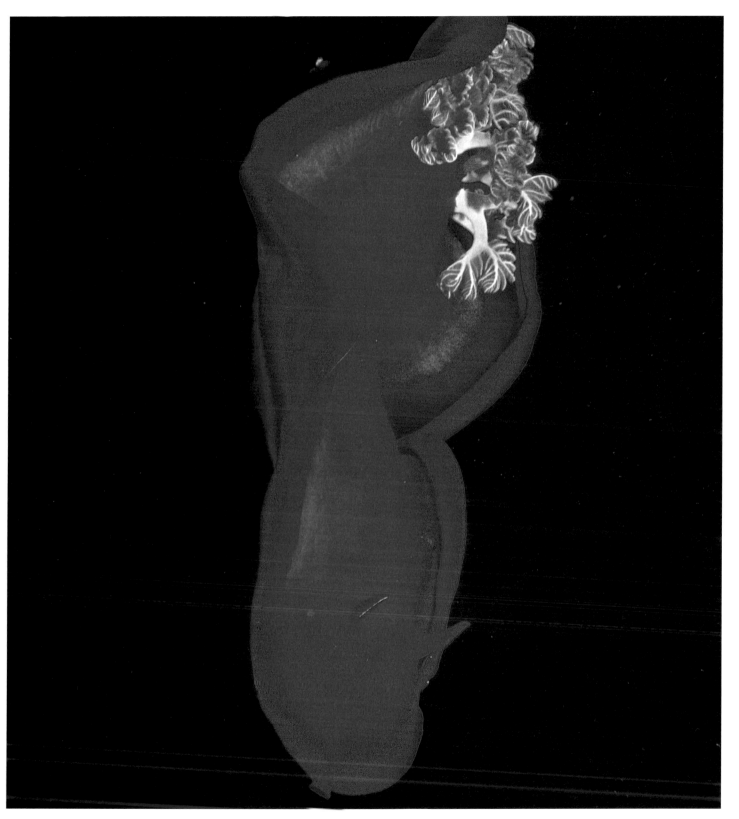

SPANISH DANCER

The Spanish dancer (*Hexabranchus sanguineus*) is the largest Nuf the nudibranch family. It is poisonous, and so has bright red warning coloration.